Fragment from an original Maimonidean Hebrew manuscript

Moses Maimonides'
Treatise on Asthma

Moses Maimonides'
Treatise on Asthma

Maimonides'
Medical Writings

translated and annotated by

Fred Rosner, M.D.

with bibliography by
Jacob I. Dienstag

יד הרב דוד אסף
Yad Harav David Assaf

published by

The Maimonides Research Institute
HAIFA   ISRAEL

published by

The Maimonides Research Institute

World Center of Maimonides Research
3 Rabbi David Assaf St., P.O.B. 9049
Mount Carmel, Haifa 31090, Israel

This Volume, **Treatise on Asthma,**
is dedicated to His Honor, His Majesty,

KING HASSAN II, King of Morocco
Patron of the
International Maimonidean Conference, 1994
held in Fes, city of Maimonides.
May the merit of Maimonides protect and shield
His Majesty and his whole family, and bless Him
with good, long and fruitful years.

On behalf of the Jewish nation, we express
our heartfelt appreciation and recognition to
His Majesty, as "Righteous Amongst the Nations"
and an ardent admirer of Maimonides.

Table of Contents

A word from the Dean

"נותן נשמה לעם עליה ורוח
להולכים בה" (ישעיה מ"ב, ה)

*"He that giveth breath unto
the people of the earth and
spirit to them that walk
therein"* (Isaiah 42, 5)

Endowed by the breath of life, man became a living soul.

Like heaven and earth, breath and soul complement each
other in perfect harmony, as illustrated by their common root
— Neshimah and Neshamah respectively. "Wonders of
wonders" exclaimed the Ramah, famous 15th century Bible
commentator, "how the spiritual soul fuses with the physical
body to create a human being."

From the moment of birth until the end of our days, our very
life depends on the smooth, uninterrupted flow of air into and
out of our lungs. We offer, therefore, our nightly prayer of
thanks — the "HaMapil" Benediction and "Bedtime Shema"
— for the gift of sleep, to invoke the heavenly blessing of the
continuous, delicately-balanced process of drawing in and
releasing the thinnest and most invisible substance of our body,
also during our dormant hours.

Following the vital need to alleviate in good time any
harmful effect of respiratory impairment, of labored breathing
and a sense of constriction in the chest, Moses Maimonides
dedicated this entire volume to the causes and cure of Asthma
and its implications, and he did so in the elevated spirit of
Jeremiah's prophecy (33, 6): "Behold, I will bring it

healing and cure... and will reveal unto them the abundance of peace and truth."

God created the world through a breath, and through a breath it is preserved — as expounded in Zohar Bereshit — the breath of those who assiduously study the Torah, the sanctifying source of all life and action, the source of the eternal truth inseparably linked with the eternity of the Jewish people.

For "You are My servant, Israel, in whom I will be glorified", as so gracefully rendered in the Hymn of Glory:

> My meditation day and night
> May it be pleasant in Thy sight
> For Thou art all my soul's delight.

* * *

This volume is dedicated to His Majesty, King Hassan II, King of Morrocco. King Hassan II was most gracious Patron of the historical Maimonides Institute's 1994 Conference, which was held in Fes, the city of Maimonides.

This dedication was initiated at the suggestion of our long-time friend and benefactor of the Institute and Kollel Od Yosef Chai, Mr. Clement Vaturi, Chairman of the European Section of the Institute.

This volume has been translated and annotated, as were its predecessors, by the prominent physician and Maimonidean authority, Dr. Fred Rosner, whose lengthy association with the Institute is a source of pride.

Our heartfelt thanks are extended to Professor Rabbi Jacob I. Dienstag, world-famous Maimonidean scholar and a dear and close friend of my late father, of blessed memory, for the preparation of the bibliographies included herein.

We are also indebted to Rabbi Yehoshua Woolf, a member of the Board of this Institute, for his inmense effort in preparing an all-embracing index, offering readers a valuable guide of reference. And last but not least, our thanks and appreciation go to Mr. Shaul Yehuda for editing this book with a keen insight and an unusual degree of perception as well as to Mr. Mordechai Avni (Wahnich) for his devotion and meticulous type-setting work.

Rabbi YEHUDA ASSAF
Dean
The Maimonides Research Institute

PREFACE

The present volume is the sixth in the series of the medical writings of Moses Maimonides. In 1984, the Maimonides Research Institute published my English translations of Maimonides' *Treatises on Poisons, Hemorrhoids and Cohabitation* in a single volume. Three years later, the Institute published the first ever English version of Maimonides' **Commentary on the Aphorisms of Hippocrates.** The most voluminous of Maimonides' medical works, his *Medical Aphorisms*, was published as volume three in the series.

The fourth volume, published in 1990, comprises Maimonides' famous *Regimen of Health (Regimine Sanitatis),* his *Treatise on the Causes of Symptoms*, often considered to be a continuation of the *Regimen of Health*, and Maimonides' *Laws of Human Temperaments (Hilchot De'ot)* from his classic code of Jewish Law, the *Mishneh Torah*. In 1992, volume five was published. It is entitled *The Art of Cure: Extracts from Galen* and was translated from the original Arabic by Uriel S. Barzel, M.D.

The present volume represents Maimonides' recommendations to a member of the royal family of the Sultan of Egypt who suffered from asthma. Maimonides' medical genius is readily apparent in his *Treatise on Asthma*. His logical and systematic approach to the prevention, diagnosis, and treatment of illness is typical of all his medical and other writings. His allusion to psychosomatic medicine and his discussion of iatrogenic disease were far ahead of his time. His teachings that a bad physician is worse than none, that one should treat patients and not diseases, and that *primum non nocere*, among others, should be taken to heart by all students of medicine and medical practitioners of the present era.

I offer my sincere thanks to noted Maimonidean scholar and bibliographer, Professor Jacob I. Dienstag for providing the bibliography. I am also indebted to Rabbi Yehuda Assaf and Rabbi Shaul Yehuda of the Maimonides Research Institute for their support and assistance in guiding to fruition the publication of this book. I am also grateful to Rabbi Jacob Wolf for preparing the index, to Mr. Mordechai (Wahnich) **Avni for the typeseting, and to Mrs. Annette Carbone for** typing the manuscript. Finally, I acknowledge my affection and devotion to my cherished wife, Saranne and to my beloved children, Mitchel and Lydia, Miriam and Motty, Aviva and Michael, and Shalom for their support and patience during the many hours I devoted to this book rather than to them.

FRED ROSNER, M.D.
New York City

THE MEDICAL WRITINGS OF MOSES MAIMONIDES

FOREWORD

by

FRED ROSNER, M.D., F.A.C.P.

Moses, son of Maimon (Rambam in Hebrew, Abu Imram Musa Ibn Maimun in Arabic and Maimonides in Greek) was born in Cordova, Spain, on March 30, 1135 corresponding to Passover eve of the Hebrew year 4895. His mother died in childbirth and, consequently, his father *Dayan* (judge) Maimon raised him. Persecution by the Almochades (Almoravids), a fanatical Moslem group from North and West Africa, forced the Maimon family to flee Cordova in the year 1148. The family wandered through southern Spain and northern Africa for the next ten years and finally settled in Fez, Morocco.

Little is known of Maimonides' early life and medical education. There are no sources indicating that Maimonides had any formal medical education. In his *Medical Aphorisms*, (see below), he mentions "the elders before whom I have read;" this is the only allusion to some semi-private study of medicine. A few times he mentions the son of Ibn Zuhr from whom he heard teachings of the latter's illustrious father (the great physician Abu Merwan Ibn Zuhr) whom Maimonides held in great esteem.

Maimonides must have been an avid reader since his medical writings show a profound knowledge of ancient Greek authors in Arabic translations, and Moslem medical works. Hippocrates, Galen and Aristotle were his Greek medical inspirations and Rhazes of Persia, Al Farabi, and Ibn Zuhr the Spanish-Arabic physician are Moslem authors frequently quoted by Maimonides.

The Maimon family left Morocco in 1165, traveled to Palestine, landing in Acco, and from there to Egypt where they settled in Fostat (old Cairo). Maimonides turned to medicine as a livelihood only after the death of his father in 1166 and the death of his brother in a shipwreck shortly thereafter. Maimonides was left with his brother's wife and child to support and, after a year's illness following his father's death, entered into the practice of medicine. In 1174, at age 39, he was appointed Court Physician to Visier Al-Fadhil, Regent of Egypt during the absence of the Sultan, Saladin the Great, who was fighting in the Crusades in Palestine. It was at this time that Richard the Lion-Hearted, also fighting in the Crusades, is reported to have invited Maimonides to become his personal physician, an offer which Maimonides declined. His reputation as a physician grew in Egypt and neighboring countries and his fame as theologian and philosopher became worldwide.

In 1193, Saladin died and his eldest son, Al Afdal Nur ad Din Ali, a playboy, succeeded him. As a result, Maimonides' medical duties became even heavier as described in the famous letter he wrote to his friend, disciple and translator, French Rabbi Samuel Ibn Tibbon, in the year 1199:

> "...I live in Fostat and the Sultan Resides in Cairo; these two places are two Sabbath limits [marked off areas around a town within which it is permitted to move on the Sabbath; approximately one and one-half miles] distant from each other. My duties to the Sultan are very heavy. I am obliged to visit him every day, early in the morning, and when he or any of his children or

concubines are indisposed, I cannot leave Cairo but must stay during most of the day in the palace. It also frequently happens that one or two of the officers fall sick and I must attend to their healing. Hence, as a rule, every day, early in the morning, I go to Cairo and, even if nothing unusual happens there, I do not return to Fostat until the afternoon. Then I am famished but I find the antechambers filled with people, both Jews and Gentiles, nobles and common people, judges and policemen, friends and enemies, — a mixed multitude who await the time of my return.

I dismount from my animal, wash my hands, go forth to my patients, and entreat them to bear with me while I partake of some light refreshment, the only meal I eat in twenty-four hours. Then I go to attend to my patients and write prescriptions and directions for their ailments. Patients go in and out until nightfall, and sometimes, even as the Torah is my faith, until two hours and more into the night. I converse with them and prescribe for them even while lying down from sheer fatigue. When night falls, I am so exhausted that I can hardly speak.

In consequence of this, no Israelite can converse with me or befriend me [on religious or community matters] except on the Sabbath. On that day, the whole congregation, or at least the majority, comes to me after the morning service, when I instruct them as to their proceedings during the whole week. We study together a little until noon, when they depart. Some of them return and read with me after the afternoon services until evening prayer. In this manner, I spend the days. I have here related to you only a part of what you would see if you were to visit me..."

Maimonides was also the spiritual leader of the Jewish community of Egypt. At age 33, in the year 1168, shortly after settling in Fostat (old Cairo), he completed his first major work, the *Commentary on the Mishnah*. In 1178, ten years later, his *magnum opus*, the *Mishneh Torah* was finished. This monumental work is a 14-book compilation of all biblical and talmudic law and remains a classic to this day. In 1190, Maimonides' great philosophical masterpiece, the *Guide for the Perplexed* was completed.

Maimonides died on December 13, 1204 (*Tebet* 20, 4965 in the Hebrew calendar), and was buried in Tiberias. Legend relates that Maimonides' body was placed upon a donkey and the animal set loose. The donkey wandered and wandered and finally stopped in Tiberias. That is the site where the great Maimonides was buried.

Maimonides was a prolific writer. We have already mentioned his famous trilogy, the *Commentary on the Mishnah,* the *Mishneh Torah* and the *Guide for the Perplexed.* Each of these works alone would have indelibly recorded Maimonides' name for posterity. However, in addition to these, he also wrote a *Book on Logic (Ma'amar Hahigayon),* a *Book of Commandments (Sefer Hamitzvot),* an *Epistle to Yemen (Iggeret Teman),* a *Letter on Apostasy (Iggeret Hashmad),* a *Treatise on Resurrection (Ma'amar Techiyat Hametim),* commentaries on several tractates of the Talmud, and over 600 Responsa. Several additional works including the so-called *Prayer of Maimonides*[1] are attributed to him but are, in fact, spurious, the prayer having been written in 1783.

Over and above all the books just enumerated, Maimonides also wrote ten medical works.[2-3] The following is a brief examination and analysis of these medical writings. The first is called *Extracts from Galen* or *The Art of Cure.* Galen's medical writings consist of over 100 books and required two volumes just to catalogue and index them all. Maimonides, therefore, extracted what he considered the most important of Galen's pronouncements and compiled them in a small work which was intended primarily for the use of students of Greek medicine. This work, as all of Maimonides' medical books, was originally written in Arabic. This work had heretofore never been published in any language, but brief excerpts therefrom in both English and Hebrew appeared in a Hebrew periodical.[4] complete English translation by Uriel Barzel was published in 1992 as volume five of the Maimonides Research Institute Series.

The second of Maimonides' medical writings is the *Commentary on the Aphorisms of Hippocrates*. The famous aphorisms of Hippocrates were translated from the Greek into Arabic by Hunain Ibn Izchak in the ninth century. Maimonides wrote his commentary on this translation. Two incomplete Arabic manuscripts exist. A good medieval translation into Hebrew was made by Moses ben Samuel Ibn Tibbon. In this work, Maimonides occasionally criticizes both Hippocrates and Galen where either of these Greeks differ from his own views. For example, in chapter five, Hippocrates is quoted as having said, "a boy is born from the right ovary, a girl from the left", to which Maimonides remarks: "A man should be either prophet or genius to know this". The introduction to this work was edited in the original Arabic with two Hebrew and one German translations by Steinschneider in 1894.[5] The entire work was published by Hasida in 1935[6] and again in a definitive edition by Muntner in 1961.[7] Bar Sela and Hoff published Maimonides' interpretation of the first aphorism of Hippocrates.[8] This is the famous aphorism which has been called the motto or credo of the art of medicine: "Life is short, and the art long, the occasion fleeting, experience fallacious and judgment difficult. The physician must not only be prepared to do what is right himself, but must also make the patient, the attendant and the externals cooperate". I published Maimonides' *Introduction* to this work[9] as well as the entire work[10] in English as volume two of the Maimonides Research Institute Series.

The third of Maimonides' medical works, the most voluminous of all, is the *Medical Aphorisms of Moses (Pirké*

Moshe). This book is comprised of fifteen hundred aphorisms based mainly on Greek medical writers. There are twenty five chapters each dealing with a different area of medicine including anatomy, physiology, pathology, symptomatology, and diagnosis, etiology of disease and therapeutics, fevers, bloodletting or phlebotomy, laxatives and emetics, surgery, gynecology, hygiene, exercise, bathing, diet, drugs and medical curiosities. A complete Arabic original manuscript exists in the Gotha Library in East Germany. A Hebrew translation was made in the thirteenth century and published in Lemberg, Poland in 1834 and again in Vilna in 1888.[11] The definitive Hebrew edition is that of Muntner dated 1959.[12] Maimonides' Aphorisms[13] were also translated into Latin in the thirteenth century and appeared as incunabulae in Bologne in 1489 and again in Venice in 1497, followed by several printed Latin editions.[14] Only small fragments of this work appeared in a Western language[15-18] until the complete English version by myself and Muntner was published in two volumes[19-20] and reprinted.[21] My revised and improved translation of Maimonides' *Medical Aphorisms* was published in 1990 as part of the Maimonides Research Institute Series.

A few excerpts from this most important work will give the reader the flavor of Maimonidean medical thinking. Maimonides speaks of cerebrovascular disease: "one can prognosticate regarding a stroke, called apoplexy. If the attack is severe, he will certainly die but if it is minor, then cure is possible, though difficult... the worst situation that can occur following a stroke is the complete irreversible suppression of respiration..."

Maimonides explains that diabetes mellitus was seldom seen in "cold" Europe whereas it was frequently encountered in "warm" Africa. He also reports this disease to be associated with the imbibition of suave water of the Nile (Maimonides lived in Fostat or old Cairo). There follows the English translation of this most important aphorism, No. 69, from the eighth chapter: "Moses says: I, too, have not seen it in the West [Spain, where Maimonides was born and/or Morocco where he fled from the persecution of the Almochades] nor did any one of my teachers under whom I studied mention that they had seen it [diabetes]. However, here in Egypt, in the course of approximately ten years, I have seen more than twenty people who suffered from this illness. This brings one to the conclusion that this illness occurs mostly in warm countries. Perhaps the waters of the Nile, because of their suaveness, may play a role in this."

A very accurate description of obstructive emphysema is provided during a lengthy discussion of respiratory disease: "...reason [for respiratory embarrassment] is narrowing of the organs of respiration, then the breast is seen to greatly expand. This expansion produces rapid and cut off [respirations]..."

Clubbing of the fingers associated with pulmonary disease, already described by Hippocrates, is beautifully depicted: "With an illness affecting the lungs called '*hasal*'; namely, phthisis, there develops rounding of the nail as a rainbow." The signs and symptoms of pneumonia are remarkably accurately described: "The basic symptoms which occur in pneumonia and which are never lacking are as follows: acute fever, sticking [pleuritic] pain in the side, short rapid breaths, serrated pulse and cough, mostly [associated] with sputum...". Hepatitis is just as beautifully described: "The signs of liver inflammation are eight in number as follows: high fever, thirst, complete anorexia, a tongue which is initially red and then turns black, biliary vomitus, initially yellow egg yolk in color which later turns dark green, pain on the right side which ascends up to the clavicle... Occasionally a mild cough may occur and a sensation of heaviness which is first felt on the right side and then spreads widely..."

So much for the *Medical Aphorisms of Moses.*[22]

The fourth of Maimonides' medical writings is his *Treatise on Hemorrhoids*. This work was written for a nobleman, as

Maimonides describes in the introduction, probably a member of the Sultan's family. There are seven chapters dealing with normal digestion, foods harmful to patients with hemorrhoids, beneficial foods, general and local therapeutic measures such as sitz baths, oils and fumigations. Maimonides disapproves of bloodletting or surgery for hemorrhoids except in very severe cases. Maimonides' whole approach to the problem seems to bespeak a modern medical trend. The *Treatise on Hemorrhoids* was first published by Kroner in 1911 in Arabic, Hebrew and German.[23] A general description of the work in English appeared in 1927 by Bragman.[24] The definitive Hebrew edition is that of Muntner dated 1965,[25] and an English translation of the entire work was published by myself and Muntner.[26] An improved, more fully annotated English translation was recently published as part of the Maimonides Research Institute Series.[27]

In the introduction to this work, Maimonides describes the reason for writing it:

> "There was a youth, [descended] from knowledge-able, intelligent and comprehending forebears, from a prominent and renowned family, distinguished and charitable and of great means, in whom the affliction of hemorrhoids occurred at the mouth of the rectum, that interested me in his problem and placed the task [of healing them] upon me. These irritated him on some occasions and he treated them in the customary therapeutic manner until the pain subsided and the prolapsed rectum [literally: excesses that protruded] became reduced and returned to the interior of the body so that his [bodily] functions returned to normal. Because this [illness] recurred many times, he considered having them extirpated in order to uproot this malady from its source so that it not return again. I informed him of the danger inherent in this, in that it is not clear if these hemorrhoids [literally: additions] are of the variety which should be excised or not,

since there are people in whom they have once been
[surgically] extirpated and in whom other hemorrhoids
develop. This is because the causes which gave rise to
the original ones remained and, therefore, new ones
develop."

Here Maimonides provides an insight into the etiology of
disease in general in that he regards operative excision of
hemorrhoids with skepticism, because surgery does not remove
the underlying causes which produced the hemorrhoids in the
first place.

The fifth work is Maimonides' *Treatise on Sexual Intercourse*
written for the nephew of Saladin, the Sultan al Muzaffar Umar
Ibn Nur Ad-Din. The Sultan indulged heavily in sexual
activities and asked Maimonides, his physician, to aid him in
increasing his sexual potential. The work consists mainly of
recipes of foods and drugs which are either aphrodisiac or
antiaphrodisiac in their actions. Maimonides advises
moderation in sexual intercourse and describes the physiology
of sexual temperaments. There are two versions to this book, a
short authentic and a longer spurious version. Both were first
edited and published by Kroner in 1906 in Hebrew and
German.[28] Ten years later, Kroner published the true short
version from the original Arabic manuscript in Granada.[29] An
Italian edition appeared in 1906,[30] and English[31] and Spanish[32]
translations were published in 1961. The definitive Hebrew
edition of both authentic[33] and spurious[34] versions of
Maimonides' book on sex is that of Muntner dated 1965. A new
English translation of the true work by myself was published[35]
and reprinted as part of the first volume of the Maimonides'
Research Institute Series.

The sixth medical book of Moses Maimonides is his *Treatise
on Asthma*. The patient for whom this book is written suffers
from violent headaches which prevent him from wearing a
turban. The patient's symptoms begin with a common cold,
especially in the rainy season, forcing him to gasp for air until

phlegm is expelled. The patient asks whether a change of climate might be beneficial. Maimonides, in thirteen chapters, explains the rules of diet and climate in general and those rules specifically suited for asthmatics. He outlines the recipes of foods and drugs and describes the various climates of the Middle East. He states that the dry Egyptian climate is efficacious for sufferers from this disease and warns against the use of very powerful remedies. The first critical edition of this work appeared in Hebrew in 1940, edited by Muntner.[36] Additional manuscripts became available after World War II and a corrected, improved and revised, second Hebrew edition appeared in 1963.[37] Only three hundred copies of this edition were printed and thus a third edition was published by Muntner in 1965.[38] An English version of Maimonides' book on asthma was published in 1963[39] and a French translation in 1965.[40] I have commented extensively on this work elsewhere,[41-42] and this is the work which is presented in the current volume of the Maimonides Research Institute Series.

The last chapter of this work deals with concise admonitions and aphorisms which Maimonides considered "useful to any man desirous of preserving his health and administering to the sick". The chapter begins as follows: "The first thing to consider... is the provision of fresh air, clean water and a healthy diet." Fresh air is described in some detail: "...City air is stagnant, turbid and thick, the natural result of its big buildings, narrow streets, the refuse of its inhabitants... one should at least choose for a residence a wide-open site... living quarters are best located on an upper floor... and ample sunshine... Toilets should be located as far as possible from living rooms. The air should be kept dry at all times by sweet scents, fumigation and drying agents. The concern for clean air is the foremost rule in preserving the health of one's body and soul." Let our air pollution control programmers take cognizance of Maimonides' prophetic statements nearly 800 years ago.

The seventh medical work of Maimonides is his *Treatise on Poisons and Their Antidotes.* It is one of the most interesting and popular works because it is very scientific and modern in its approach and was, therefore, used as a textbook of toxicology throughout the middle ages. The book was written at the request of Maimonides' noble protector, the Grand Vizier and Supreme Judge Al Fadhil, who, in 1199, asked Maimonides to write a treatise on poisons for the layman by which to be guided before the arrival of a physician. In the introduction, Maimonides praises Al Fadhil and his feats in war and peace. He mentions Al Fadhil's orders to import from distant lands ingredients lacking in Egypt but necessary for the preparation of two antidotes against poisoning, the "great theriac" and the "electuary of Mithridates".

The first section of the book deals with snake and dog bites and with scorpion, bee, wasp, and spider stings. The first chapter concerns the conduct of the victim in general. Thus Maimonides states as follows:

> When someone is bitten, immediate care should be taken to tie the spot above the wound as fast as possible to prevent the poison from spreading throughout the body; in the meantime, another person should make cuts with a black lancet directly above the wound, suck vigorously with his mouth and spit out. Before doing that, it is advisable to disinfect the mouth with olive oil, or with spirit in oil... Care should be taken that the sucking person has no wound in his mouth, or rotten teeth... should there be no man available to do the sucking, cupping-glasses should be applied, with or without fire; the heated ones have a much better effect because they combine the advantages of sucking and cauterizing at the same time... Then apply the great theriac... Apply to the wound some medicine which should draw the poison out of the body.

In his book on poisons, Maimonides also describes the long incubation period for rabies (up to forty days). Numerous Arabic, Hebrew, and Latin manuscripts are extant.[43] A

German translation was published in 1873 by Steinschneider.[44] A French translation appeared in 1865 by Rabbinowicz and was reprinted in 1935.[45] An English translation of Steinschneider's German version is that of Bragman in 1926.[46] The definitive Hebrew edition of Muntner appeared in 1942[47] and Muntner's English version was published in 1966.[48] I commented on this work[49] and published a fully annotated new English translation with commentary and bibliography as part of the first volume of the Maimonides' Research Institute Series.

The eighth book is the *Regimen of Health (Regimen Sanitatis)* which Maimonides wrote in 1198 during the first year of the reign of Sultan Al Malik Al Afdhal, eldest son of Saladin the Great. The Sultan was a frivolous and pleasure-seeking man of thirty, subject to fits of melancholy or depression due to his excessive indulgences in wine and women, and his warlike adventures against his own relatives and in the Crusades. He complained to his physician of constipation, dejection, bad thoughts and indigestion. Maimonides answered his royal patient in four chapters. The first chapter is a brief abstract on diet taken mostly from Hippocrates and Galen. The second chapter deals with advice on hygiene, diet and drugs in the absence of a physician. The third extremely important chapter contains Maimonides' concept of "a healthy mind in a healthy body", one of the earliest descriptions of psychosomatic medicine. He indicates that the physical well-being of a person is dependent on his mental well-being and vice versa. The final chapter summarizes his prescriptions relating to climate, domicile, occupation, bathing, sex, wine drinking, diet and respiratory infections.

The whole treatise on the *Regimen of Health* is short and concise but to the point. This is the reason for its great success and popularity throughout the years. It is extant in numerous manuscripts. A Hebrew translation from the original Arabic was made by Moses ben Samuel Ibn Tibbon in 1244 and this version was reprinted several times in the nineteenth century (Prague 1838, Jerusalem 1885, Warsaw 1886). Two Latin translations were made in the thirteenth century. Several fifteenth century incunabulae and sixteenth century editions of these Latin versions exist. One of the first Hebrew editions is that of Bloch in 1838.[50] An annotated German translation by Winternitz was published in 1843,[51] and Russian[52] and Spanish[53] translations in 1930 and 1961, respectively. The Arabic text with German and Hebrew translations was published by Kroner in 1925,[54] although he had already published the all-important third chapter, dealing with psychosomatic medicine, eleven years earlier, in 1914.[55]

English translations of chapter three have been published by Bragman,[56] Savitz,[57] and Butterworth[58] and of the first two chapters by Skoss.[59] The definitive Hebrew edition is that of Muntner, dated 1957,[60] although the Maimonidean biblio-grapher Dienstag[61] cites several additional Hebrew editions. Three English translations of the entire work were published: in 1958 by Gordon,[62] in 1964 by Bar Sela, Hoff and Faris,[63] and in 1990 as part of the first volume of the Maimonides' Research Institute Series. Another German translation by Muntner appeared in 1966.[64] These numerous editions in many languages attest to the importance and popularity of Maimonides' *Regimen of Health.*

The ninth medical writing of Maimonides is the *Discourse on the Explanation of Fits.* This work has been called Maimonides' swan song as it was thought to be the last of his medical works, having been written in the year 1200, four years before his death. It was also written for the Sultan Al Malik Al Afdhal and is sometimes considered to represent chapter five of the *Regimen of Health.* The Sultan persisted in his over-indulgences and wrote to Maimonides, who was himself ill, asking advice about his health. Maimonides confirms most of the pre-scriptions of the Sultan's other physicians regarding wine, laxatives, bathing, exercise and the like and, near the end, gives a very detailed hour by hour regimen for the daily life of the Sultan. The original Arabic was edited and published with Hebrew and German translations by Kroner in 1928.[65] English editions by Bar Sela, Hoff and Faris in 1964,[63] and myself and Muntner in 1969,[26] another German version by Muntner in 1966,[64] and another Hebrew edition by Muntner in 1969[66] are available. A very good edition is that by Leibowitz and Marcus entitled "On the Causes of Symptoms",[67] in which the text is presented in four languages (Arabic, Hebrew, Latin and English) and is accompanied by a running commentary, explanatory essays and a comprehensive catalogue of drugs. This work was also republished in a revised version as part of volume four of the Maimonides' Research Institute Series.

The final authentic medical book of Maimonides is the *Glossary of Drug Names.* This work was discovered by Max Meyerhof, an ophthalmologist in Egypt, in the Aya Sofia library in Istanbul, Turkey as Arabic manuscript No. 3711.[68-69] Dr. Meyerhof edited the original Arabic and provided a French translation with a detailed commentary which he published in 1940 in Cairo.[70] A Hebrew edition by Muntner appeared in 1969[66] and my English translation was published in 1979.[71] The work is essentially a pharmacopeia and consists of four hundred and five short paragraphs containing names of drugs in Arabic, Greek, Syrian, Persian, Berber and Spanish.

In summary, Maimonides' medical writings are varied, comprising extracts from Greek medicine, a series of monographs on health in general and several diseases in particular, and a recently discovered pharmacopeia demonstrating Maimonides' extensive knowledge of Arabic medical literature and his familiarity with several languages. Some people feel that Maimonides' medical writings are not as original as his theological and philosophical writings. However, his medical works demonstrate the same lucidity, conciseness and formidable powers of systematization and organization so characteristic of all his writings. The *Book on Poisons,* the *Regimen of Health,* and the *Medical Aphorisms of Maimonides* became classics in their fields of medieval times.

I conclude by citing a paragraph from my first paper on Maimonides:[72]

"Maimonides died on December 13, 1204 [Tebeth 20, 4965 in the Hebrew calendar] and was buried in Tiberias, Palestine. The Christian, Moslem and Jewish worlds mourned him. His literary ability was incredible and his knowledge encyclopedic. He mastered nearly everything known in the field of theology, mathematics, law, philosophy, astronomy, ethics, and, of course, medicine. As a physician, he treated disease by the scientific method, not by guesswork, superstition, or rule of thumb. His attitude towards the practice of medicine came from his deep religious background, which made the preservation of health and life a divine commandment. His inspiration lives on through the years and his position as one of the medical giants of history is indelibly recorded. He was physician to Sultans and Princes, and as Sir William Osler said, 'He was Prince of Physicians'. The heritage of his great medical writings is being more and more appreciated. To the Jewish people he symbolized the highest spiritual and intellectual achievement of man on this earth; as so aptly stated, 'From Moses to Moses there never arose a man like Moses', and none has since."

REFERENCES

1. Rosner, F.: The Physician's Prayer Attributed to Maimonides. *Bull. Hist. Med. 41:* 440-454, 1967.

2. Rosner, F.: Maimonides, the Physician: A Bibliography. *Bull. Hist. Med. 43:* 221-235, 1969.

3. Rosner, F.: Maimonides the Physician: A Bibliography. *Clio Medica 15:* 75-79, 1980.

4. Barzel, U.: The Art of Cure: A Non-Published Medical Book by Maimonides. *Harofe Haivri 2:* 82-83 (Hebr.) and 177-165 (Eng.) 1955.

5. Steinschneider, M. : Die Vorrede des Maimonides zu seinem Commentar uber die Aphorismen des Hippokrates. *Ztschr. d. deutsch. Morganland. Gessellsch. 48:* 213-234, 1894.

6. Hasida (Bocian), M.Z.: *Perush lepirké Abukrat shel Ha-Rambam. Hassegullah* (Jerusalem) 1934-5, nos. 1-30 (Stencil) (Hebr.).

7. Muntner, S.: *Mosheh ben Maimon.* Commentary on the Aphorisms of Hippocrates. *Perush lepirkei Abukrat.* Jerusalem: Mossad Harav Kook, 1961. XIV + 166 pp.

8. Bar Sela, a. and Hoff, H.E.: Maimonides' Interpretation of the First Aphorism of Hippocrates. *Bull. Hist. Med. 37:* 347-354, 1968.

9. Rosner, F.: The Introduction of Maimonides to his "Commentary on the Aphorisms of Hippocrates". *Clio Medica 11:* 59-64, 1976.

10. Rosner, F.: *Moses Maimonides' Commentary on the Aphorisms of Hippocrates.* Haifa. Maimonides Research Institute, 1987.

11. Magid, Z. Ed. Medical Aphorisms of Maimonides *(Pirké Moshe).* Vilna: L. Matz, 1888, 112 pp. (1st ed. Lemberg 1834) (Hebr.).

12. Muntner, S.: *Moshe ben Maimon. (Medical) Aphorisms of Moses in Twenty-Five Treatises (Pirké Moshe Birefuah).* Jerusalem: Mossad Harav Kook, 1959, XXXII + 470 (Hebr.: Eng. summary).

13. Leibowitz, J.O.: Maimonides' Aphorisms, *Koroth 1:* 213-219 (Hebr.); I-III (Engl. Summary) 1955.

14. Leibowitz, J.O.: The Latin Translations of Maimonides' Aphorisms. *Koroth 6:* 273-281 (Hebr.); XCIII-XCIV (Engl. summary) 1973.

15. Steinberg, W. and Muntner, S.: Maimonides' Views on Gynecology and Obstetrics. *Am. J. Obst. Gynec. 91:* 443-448, 1965.

16. Rosner, F. and Muntner, S.: Moses Maimonides' Aphorisms Regarding Analysis of Urine. *Ann. Int. Med. 71:* 217-220, 1969.

17. Rosner, F. and Muntner, S.: The Surgical Aphorisms of Moses Maimonides. *Amer. J. Surg. 119:* 718-725, 1970.

18. Rosner, F.: Moses Maimonides & Diseases of the Chest. *Chest 60:* 68-72, 1971.

19. Rosner, F. and Muntner, S.: Studies in Judaica. *The Medical Aphorisms of Moses Maimonides,* New York. Yeshiva Univ. Press, 1970 Vol. 1, pp. 267.

20. Rosner, F. and Muntner, S.: Studies in Judaica. *The Medical Aphorisms of Moses Maimonides,* New York. Yeshiva Univ. Press, 1971 Vol. 2, pp. 244.

21. Rosner, F. and Muntner, S.: Studies in Judaica. *The Medical Aphorisms of Moses Maimonides,* Vol. I and Vol. II, New York, Bloch Publishing Co., for Yeshiva Univ. Press 1973, pp. 264 and 244.

22. Rosner, F.: The Medical Aphorisms of Moses Maimonides, in *Memorial Volume in Honor of S. Muntner.* (Edit. J.O. Leibowitz). Israel Inst. Hist. Med. Jerusalem, 1983, pp. 6-30.

23. Kroner, H.: Die Haemorrhoiden in der Medicin XII und XIII. Jahrhunderts. *Janus 16:* 441-456 and 644-718, 1911.

24. Bragman, L.J.: Maimonides' Treatise on Hemorrhoids. *New York State Med. J. 27:* 598-601, 1927.

25. Muntner, S.: *Moshe ben Maimon. On Hemorrhoids (Birefuoth Hatechorim).* Jerusalem: Mossad Harav Kook, 1965. 32 pp. (Hebr.).

26. Rosner, F. and Muntner, S.: *The Medical Writings of Moses Maimonides. Treatise on Hemorrhoids and Maimonides' Answers to Queries.* Philadelphia: Lippincott, 1969, XV and 79 pp.

27. Rosner, F.: *Moses Maimonides' Treatises on Poisons, Hemorrhoids, and Cohabitation.* Haifa. Maimonides Research Institute, 1984.

28. Kroner, H.: *Ein Betrag zur Geschichte der Medizin des XII Jahrhunderts an der Hand Zweier Medizinischer Abhandlungen des Maimonides auf Grund von 6 unedierten Handschriften.* Oberdorf-Bopfingen: Itzowski, 1906, 116 pp. (Ger.), 28 pp. (Hebr.).

29. Kroner, H.: Eine Medizinische Maimonides Handschrift aus Granada. Ein Beitrag zur Stilistik des Maimonides und Charakteristik der Hebraischen Ueberzetzungsliteratur. *Janus 21:* 203-247, 1916.

30. DeMartini, U.: Maimonides. *Segreto dei segreti.* Rome: Instituto de storia della Medicina dell'Universita de Roma, 1960, 84 pp.

31. Gorlin, M.: *Maimonides "On Sexual Intercourse". (Fi'l-Jima).* Brooklyn, N.Y.: Rambash Publ., 1961, 128 pp.

32. Chelminski, E.: Notas introductorias al "Guia sobre el contacto sexual" de Maimonides. *Anales de ars Medici* (Mexico) *5*(4): 240-248, 1961.

33. Muntner, S.: *Moshe ben Maimon on the Increase of Physical Vigour (Ma'amar al chizuk koach hagavra).* Jerusalem: Mossad Harav Kook, 1965, pp. 35-65 (Hebr.).

34. Muntner, S.: Pseudo-Maimonides on Sexual Life. In *Sexual Life, Collection of Medieval Treatises (Ma'amar al razei hachajim haminiyim).* Jerusalem: Geniza, 1965, 108 pp. (Hebr.).

35. Rosner, F.: *Sex Ethics in the Writings of Moses Maimonides.* New York: Bloch Publishing Co., 1974, and 129 pp.

36. Muntner, S.: *Moshe ben Maimon* (Maimonides). *Sefer Hakatzereth* (The Book on Asthma). Jerusalem: Rubin Mass. 1940, XV + 168 pp. (Hebr.).

37. Muntner, S.: *Rabbi Moses ben Maimon. Sefer Hakatzereth* or *Sefer Hamisadim* (The Book on Asthma). Jerusalem: Geniza, 1963, 56 pp. (Hebr.).

38. Muntner, S.: *Moshe ben Maimon on Asthma (Sefer Hakatzereth).* Jerusalem: Mossad Harav Kook, 1965, pp. 67-119 (Hebr.).

39. Muntner, S.: *The Medical Writings of Moses Maimonides. Treatise on Asthma.* Philadelphia: Lippincott, 1963, XXIV — 115 pp.

40. Muntner, S. and Simon, I.: Le Traité de l'Asthme de Maïmonide (1135-1204) traduit pour la première fois en Français d'après le texte Hébreu. *Rev. d'Hist. Méd. Héb. 16:* 171-186, 1963; *17:* 5-13, 83-97, 127-139, 187-196, 1964; *18:* 5-15, 1965.

41. Rosner, F.: Moses Maimonides' Treatise on Asthma. *Thorax 36:* 245-251, 1981.

42. Rosner, F.: Moses Maimonides' Treatise on Asthma. *J. Asthma 21:* 119-129, 1984.

43. Rosner, F.: Moses Maimonides' Treatise on Poisons. *J.A.M.A.* *205:* 914-916, 1968.

44. Steinschneider, M.: Gifte und ihre Heilung. *Virchows Arch. F. Path. Anat. 57:* 62-120, 1873.

45. Rabbinowicz, I.M.: *Traité des Poisons.* Paris: Lipschutz, 1935, 70 pp. (1st ed.) 1865.

46. Bragman, L.J.: Maimonides' Treatise on Poisons. *Med. J. and Rec. 124:* 103-107, 1926.

47. Muntner, S.: *Moshe ben Maimon* (Maimonides), *Samei hamaveth veharafuoth kenegdam* (Poisons and their Antidotes, or "The Treatise to the Honored One"). Jerusalem: Rubin Mass, 1942 XX + 233 pp. (Hebr.).

48. Muntner, S.: The Medical Writings of Moses Maimonides, Vol. 2: *Treatise on Poisons and Their Antidotes.* Philadelphia: Lippincott, 1966, XXXVII + 77 pp.

49. Rosner, F.: Moses Maimonides' Treatise on Poisons, *N.Y. State J. Med. 80:* 1627-1630, 1980.

50. Bloch, S.: *Michtav Harav Rabenu Moshe ben Maimon Be'ad HaSultan. Kerem Chemed 3:* 31-39, 1838.

51. Winternitz, D.: *Das Diatetische Sendschreiben des Maimonides* (Rambam) *an den Sultan Saladin.* Vienna 1843, 64 pp.

52. Shmukler, I.K.: *Pismo Moiseh Maimonida K Egipefskomu Sultanu.* Gugienicheskie Sovetia Perevod S Drevneevreiskogo Doctora I.K. Shmuklera (Kiev). Otdelnii Ottisk Iz, "Vrach Dela" #14-15 and 16. Charkov. "Nauchnaja Misl". Uchr. NKZ. UKSSR (1930).

53. Chelminsky, E. "La Preservacion de la Juventud" de Maimonides. Version Castellana. *Anales de Ars Medici* (Mexico) *5:* 303-344, 1961.

54. Kroner, H.: *Fi tadbir as sihhat.* Gesundheitsanleitung des Maimonides fur den Sultan al-Malik Al-Afdhal. *Janus 27:* 101-116, 286-330, 1923; *28:* 61-74, 143-152, 199-217, 408-419, 455-472, 1924; *29:* 235-258, 1925.

55. Kroner, H.: *Die Seelenhygiene des Maimonides. Auszug aus dem 3. Kapital des diatetischen Sendschreibens des Maimonides an den Sultan al Malik Al-Afdahl* (ca. 1198). Frankfurt A.M.: J. Kauffmann, 1914, 18 pp. (Germ.), 8 pp. (Hebr. and Arab.).

56. Bragman, L.J.: Maimonides on Physical Hygiene. *Ann. Med. Hist. 7:* 140-143, 1925.

57. Savitz, H.: Maimonides' Hygiene of the Soul. *Ann. Med. Hist. 4:* 80-86, 1932.

58. Butterworth, C.E.: On the Management of Health, in *Ethical Writings of Maimonides* (Edit. R.L. Weiss and C.E. Butterworth), New York, N.Y. Univ. Press, 1975, pp. 105-111.

59. Skoss, S.L.: The Treatises of Maimonides on Health Care. in *Portrait of a Jewish Scholar; Essays and Addresses.* New York, Bloch, 1957, pp. 99-116.

60. Muntner, S.: *Moshe ben Maimon. Hanhagath habriyuth.* Regimen sanitatis. letters on the hygiene of the body and of the soul. Jerusalem: Mossad Harav Kook, 1956, XVIII + 254 pp. (Hebr.).

61. Dienstag, J.I. Translators and Editors of Maimonides' Medical Works; A Bio-Bibliographical Survey, in *Memorial Volume in Honor of S. Muntner.* (Edit. J.O. Leibowitz). Israel Inst. His. Med. Jerusalem, 1983, pp. 95-135.

62. Gordon, H.L.: *Moses ben Maimon, The Preservation of Youth.* Essays on Health *(Fi Tadbir As-Sihha).* New York; Philos. Lib. 1958, 92 pp.

63. Bar Sela, A., Hoff, H.E. and Faris, E.: *Moses Maimonides' Two Treatises on the Regimen of Health.* Philadelphia: Am. Philos. SOc. (Trans. n.s. vol. 54, pg 4), 1964, 50 pp.

64. Muntner, S.: *Regimen Sanitatis oder Dietetik fur die Seele und den Korper mit Anhang der Medizinischen Responsen und Ethik des Maimonides.* Basel: S. Karger, 1966, 208 pp.

65. Kroner, H.: Der Medizinische Schwanengesang des Maimonides. *Janus 32:* 12-116, 1928.

66. Muntner, S.: *Moshe ben Maimon. Biyur Shaymoth Harefuoth* (Lexicography of Drugs, and Medical Responses). Jerusalem 1969 Mossad Harav Kook, 164 pp.

67. Leibowitz, J.O. and Marcus, S.: *Moses Maimonides On the Causes of Symptoms.* Berkeley. Univ. of Calif. Press 1974, 263 p.

68. Meyerhof, M.: Sur un Glossaire de Matière Médicale Arabe Composé par Maïmonide. *Bull. Inst. Egypte 17:* 223-235, 1935.

69. Meyerhof, M.: Sur un Ouvrage Médicale Inconnu de Maïmonide. *Mélanges Maspéro 3:* 1-7, 1935-1940.

70. Meyerhof, J.: *Un Glossaire de Matière Medicale, Composé par Maïmonide (Sarh Asma al'Uqqar).* Mém. Inst. Egypte, Vol. 41 LXXXVI + 256 pp.

71. Rosner, F.: *Moses Maimonides' Glossary of Drug Names.* Philadelphia. Amer. Philosoph. Soc. 1979, LXI and 364 pp.

72. Rosner, F.: Moses Maimonides (1135-1204). *Ann. Int. Med. 62:* 373-375, 1965.

MANUSCRIPTS AND PREVIOUS EDITIONS OF MAIMONIDES' TREATISE ON ASTHMA

Moses Maimonides' *Treatise on Asthma,* as all his medical works, was originally written in Arabic with the title *Makalah Pi Alrabo.* An original Arabic version with Arabic lettering is manuscript #601[9] in the Madrid library (formerly Escorial #888). Additionl Arabic manuscripts but in Hebrew letters are manuscript #1211 of the National Library in Paris and Bodleian (Neubauer) manuscript #1202 in Oxford. The Parisian catalog only lists this work with the notation "a few pages are not in proper order", but in reality Parisian manuscript #1211 also contains three other Maimonidean medical treatises, the *Treatise on Poisons,* the *Treatise on the Regimen of Health* and the *Medical Responsa.*[1]

Maimonides' *Treatise on Asthma* was twice translated into Hebrew and once into Latin. However, not all extant manuscripts in the various libraries throughout the world have been adequately studied.[2]

The first Hebrew translation in the year 1320, apparently prepared from the Latin version, is that of Samuel Benveniste, a Spanish physician from Saragossa. He was physician in the house of Don Manuel, brother of King Don Fredo the fourth of Aragonia.[3] Benveniste's translation is extant in the following manuscripts: Parma-Rossi #1208, Bologna#20[5], Paris #1173,

Paris #1175, Paris #1176, Vienna #151 (folio 163; Gold folio 86). There are differences among these manuscripts. In only one of the six manuscripts is the name of the translator (Benveniste) mentioned in chapter 12. The Vienna manuscript is briefer than the others and the Paris manuscripts are incomplete. The Bologne manuscript has the additional title *Sefer Hamisadim* (literally: book of nourishments), probably because the unknown patient for whom the book was written asked for and was given nutritional advice in regard to which foods he should select and which he should avoid and which regimen he should follow to be cured of his asthma. Steinschneider[4] points out that the *Treatise on Asthma* contains parallel phrases and verbatim wording of various sections of Maimonides' *Regimen of Health* and that a fragment of Benveniste's translation was extant in the private library of Joshua H. Schorr.

The second Hebrew translation of Maimonides' *Treatise on Asthma* is that of Joshua Shatibi from Xativa about the end of the fourteenth century. He translated directly from the original Arabic into Hebrew. Shatibi was called "the scholar in every field of knowledge, especially medicine". A copyist's note in Munich manuscript #280 states that Shatibi translated this treatise for an unknown Jewish apostate of high standing in the court of King Juan the First of Castille who reigned from 1379 to 1390. The translator did not translate the title nor much of the Arabic text except for the names of therapies. Only two manuscripts of Shatibi's Hebrew version of Maimonides' *Treatise on Asthma* are extant today: Munich Manuscript #280 folio 35 (copy also in Munich manuscript #43 from the middle of the sixteenth century) and Steinschneider manuscript #30 folio 66 to 92b. The latter is now in the national library in Berlin as manuscript #232 and also contains several other Maimonidean medical treatises including his *Commentary on the Aphorisms of Hippocrates,* his *Regimen of Health,* his *Treatise on Sexual Intercourse,* his *Treatise on Hemorrhoids,* his *Medical Responsa* and his *Medical Aphorisms of Moses.*

Maimonides' *Treatise on Asthma* was translated into Latin by Armengaud de Blaise, a French scholar, in May 1302. The Latin version exists in Cambridge (Smith Catalogue p. 92) as manuscript St. Peter, Cambridge 209[8] under the title *Tractatus Contra Passionem Asthmatis* or *DeRegimine Egrorum et Sanorum et Specialiter de Asinate* (should be *asthmate*). An additional Latin manuscript is described by Friedenwald[5] who states that this work is "not found elsewhere in Latin translation... This anonymous translation differs from that of Armengaud and is otherwise unknown". It would thus appear that this manuscript, which is now part of the Friedenwald collection of the Hebrew University in Jerusalem, differs from the Cambridge Latin manuscript described above.

Muntner writes[6] that Dr. L. Bertolot in the Vatican discovered a fifteenth century Latin manuscript containing translations of six of Maimonides' medical writings including his *Treatise on Asthma*. The others are his *Regimen of Health, Medical Responsa, Poisons and Their Antidotes, Treatise on Hemorrhoids* and *Treatise on Sexual Intercourse*. This Latin manuscript is probably identical to the Friedenwald manuscript which also contains the other five Maimonidean medical works in the same sequence. Both the Vatican and Friedenwald manuscripts begin and end with identical phrases: *Inquit Moyses filius Maymonis filii Abdelle cordubensis yspanus. Narravit nobis dominus rex... Finis. Explixit Tractatus Alrabo idest asmatis.*

Maimonides' *Treatise on Asthma* remained dormant for several hundred years until the early part of the twentieth century when Dr. Herman Kroner, Rabbi in a small town in Germany, began editing this work and translating it into German. Unfortunately, he died in 1930 before the task was completed. Ten years later, Suessman Muntner published the first critical Hebrew edition of the *Treatise on Asthma,*[7] based mainly on the Paris Hebrew manuscript #1173 which represents

Benveniste's Hebrew translation. Muntner's edition is complete with introduction, bibliography, remarks, commentary and Hebrew, Arabic, Greek and Latin indices. Also included are an analysis of Maimonides' *Treatise on Asthma,* a lengthy discussion on Maimonides the Physician, an essay on "Asthma in Ancient Hebrew Literature" and a brief chapter devoted to "Modern Views on the Pathology and Treatment of Asthma". For the non-Hebrew reader, there is also an English summary of this Maimonidean book. Muntner's Hebrew edition was commented upon by Levy[8] and reviewed by Nemoy.[9]

During the preparation of an English edition of Maimonides' *Treatise on Asthma* (see below), Muntner discovered numerous typographical and textual errors in his Hebrew edition. He, therefore, published a revised and corrected Hebrew version in 1963.[10] This second Hebrew edition was limited solely to the Hebrew text and the reader is referred to the first edition for the profuse commentaries mentioned above. Since only three hundred copies of the second edition were published, Muntner published a third version of only the Hebrew text with additional corrections.[11] This edition is bound together with critical editions of two other Maimonidean medical works, the *Treatise on Hemorrhoids* and the *Treatise on Sexual Intercourse.*

To bring the medical genius of Moses Maimonides to the attention of the modern world, Muntner translated the *Treatise on Asthma* into English.[12] This 1963 English version contains a preface by famed pediatrician Bela Schick who says: "I was impressed by the depth of Maimonides' knowledge of the disease (i.e., asthma), by the clarity of the discussion of its cause and of the influence of the environment, as well as the general health of the individual upon the disease". In an introduction to the same English version, noted allergist M. Murray Peshkin points out that "in spite of spectacular modern advances made in the theoretical and practical aspects of the allergies, the studies of the asthmatic state, written in the 12th century by Maimonides, still merit out attention".

Shortly after the appearance of the English edition of Maimonides' *Treatise on Asthma,* Muntner, in collaboration with Isidore Simon, founder and editor of the Parisian-based *Revue d'Histoire de la Médecine Hébraïque,* published a French version but without notes, commentary or index.[13]

I have previously commented upon Maimonides' *Treatise on Asthma* on three separate occasions.[14] The present edition is my English translation of Muntner's Hebrew version of 1940 as corrected in the 1963 and 1965 reprintings. This new translation is fully annotated and retains Muntner's scholarly notes and commentaries. Words in brackets are my own additions to help clarify the meaning of the text.

NOTES

1. Steinschneider, M. *Die Arabische Literatur Der Juden.* Frankfurt A.M. J. Kaufmann 1902, p. 215.

2. Steinschneider, M. *Die Hebraeischen Uebersetzungen des Mittelalters und die Juden als Dolmetscher.* Berlin 1893, pp. 767-768.

3. Muntner, S. *Rabbenu Moshe ben Maimon Sefer Hakatzereth O Sefer Hamisadim* (Treatise on Asthma or Book of Nourishments). Jerusalem. Rubin Mass, 1940, XV and 167 pp.

4. Steinschneider. see note 1.

5. Friedenwald, H. *Jewish Luminaries in Medical History.* Baltimore, Johns Hopkins Press, 1946, pp. 99-100.

6. Muntner. *loc. cit.*

7. *Ibid.*

8. Levy, A.J. *He'aroth Lesefer Hakatzereth Leharambam* (Comments on the Book of Asthma by Maimonides). *Harofé Haivri*, Vol. 2, pp. 129-132, 1940.

9. Nemoy, L. *Rabbenu Moshe ben Maimon: Sefer Hakatzereth.* (Maimonides' Treatise on Asthma) edit. S. Muntner, Jerusalem. Rubin Mass, 1940. *Harofe Haivri* Vol. 2, pp. 133-134, 1940.

10. Muntner, S. *Rabbenu Moshe ben Maimon. Sefer Hakatzereth O sefer Hamisadim* (Treatise on Asthma). Jerusalem, Geniza, 1963, 56 pp.

11. Muntner, S. *Rabbenu Moshe ben Maimon. Sefer Hakatzereth O Sefer Hamisadim* (Treatise on Asthma). Jerusalem, Mossad Harav Kook, 1965, pp. 67-119.

12. Muntner, S. *The Medical Writings of Moses Maimonides. Treatise on Asthma.* Philadelphia. Lippincott, 1963, 115 pp.

13. Muntner, S. and Simon, I. Le Traité de l'Asthme de Maïmonide (135-1204). Traduit pour la première fois en Français d'après le texte Hébreu. *Revue d'Histoire de la Médecine Hébraïque,* Vol. 16, pp. 171-186 (Dec.) 1963; Vol. 17, pp. 5-13 (March) 1964; Vol. 17, pp. 83-97 (July) 1964; Vol. 17, pp. 127-139 (Oct.) 1964; Vol. 17, pp. 187-196 (Dec.) 1964; Vol. 18, pp. 5-15 (March) 1965.

14. Rosner, F. Moses Maimonides' Treatise on Asthma. *Medical Times,* Vol. 94, pp. 1227-1230, 1966; *Thorax,* Vol. 36, pp. 245-251, 1981; *Journal of Asthma,* Vol. 21, pp. 119-129, 1984.

Page from a Latin manuscript of the *Treatise on Asthma* in the Vatican library. Translated from Hebrew by John di Capua.

SUMMARY
AND APPRECIATION
OF MAIMONIDES' TREATISE
ON ASTHMA

In the Introduction to his book, Maimonides praises his benefactors for having asked him to write this work. Maimonides points out that asthma should be treated according to the various causes that bring it about. He further states that one can only manage the disease properly if one has a thorough knowledge of the patient's constitution and his individual organs, the age and habits of the patient, the season and the climate. Maimonides asserts that in this book he intends to include general principles which might be useful to all people to preserve their health and to prevent disease. He then lists the thirteen chapters and their headings:

Chapter one advises on the best course of personal conduct in general.

Chapter two treats of the dietary measures which should be adopted or avoided when afflicted with the disease under consideration.

Chapter three treats of the foods to be taken or eschewed, with special emphasis on the foods of similar origin.

Chapter four treats of the preparation of the dishes commendable in this disease.

Chapter five treats of the quantity of food the patient may safely consume.

Chapter six treats of the number of meals to be taken in a given period of time.

Chapter seven treats of beverages.

Chapter eight treats of respiration and emotional processes.

Chapter nine treats of bowel movement, eventually of holding back of evacuation.

Chapter ten treats of habits of sleep and waking up, of bathing, massages and coitus.

Chapter eleven treats of the (simple) remedies and their use in this disease.

Chapter twelve treats of the composition of drugs which might be called for in treating this disease in line with the present treatise.

Chapter thirteen includes short summaries which might be useful to any man desirous of preserving his health and administering to the sick, in the form of concise admonitions.

In chapter one, Maimonides gives general advice regarding illnesses which are characterized by acute attacks such as arthritis, migraine, asthma, kidney stones and their like. He cites Galen who recommends dietary means to treat and even prevent these maladies. Maimonides states that hygienic principles can be grouped into seven categories of which the first six are obligatory and the seventh is commendable: clean air, correct eating and drinking, regulating of one's emotions, exercise and rest, sleep and wakefulness, excretion or retention of wastes, and bathing and massaging. To these he adds the regulation of coitus as an important factor in a general health regimen. These are discussed in detail in the subsequent chapters.

Chapter two deals with nutritional and dietary measures to be adhered to or avoided by the patient suffering from asthma. Maimonides recommends that food be consumed in moderate amounts and that it should be easily digestible. He states that a fattening diet is objectional and may endanger life, especially in an asthmatic patient. Gas-generating foods and scalding hot food should also be avoided.

In chapter three, Maimonides lists a variety of poorly digestible foods such as grossly sifted wheat flour, flour pudding, macaroni, and spaghetti, especially when these are fried in oil or treated with cane sugar or dipped in honey and fried since all flour dishes which fatten the body are detrimental because they generate thick juices which block the body vessels and passageways. Rather, flour should be finely ground and unadulterated. One should avoid gas-producing foods such as black beans, peas, rice, lentils, nuts, onion and garlic.

Maimonides also describes the virtues and detriments of a variety of other foods such as different types of meat and fowl, cheese, eggs, fish, vegetables and fruits. Chicken soup is recommended for patients suffering from asthma as are fresh water fish. Also efficacious for asthmatics are fennel, parsley, mint, pennyroyal, origanum, water cress and radish whereas lettuce, pumpkin, cauliflower and turnip are harmful. Figs, quinces and raisins in moderate amounts are beneficial whereas watermelon, peaches, apricots, cucumbers and fresh dates should be avoided.

Chapter four presents numerous recipes for the preparation of dishes helpful to the asthmatic patient. One example is a soup made from rue, beet and chicken, cooked with or without beans.

Chapter five deals with the quantity of food one should consume. This quantity varies from person to person and from season to season. A person should cease eating before experiencing a sense of repletion or fullness. Overeating is one of the prime causes of many diseases and maladies such as heartburn, diarrhea and fainting. One should also not consume a large variety of foods during a single meal. Not only are the quality and quantity of food consumed important but also the sequence of its consumption. Galen is cited as recommending that light dishes be consumed before heavy ones. Other authors are of the opposite view. Maimonides suggests that a single uniform dish, not too light or heavy, is preferred. He then points out the virtues of moderate exercise prior to eating and advises against such exercise immediately following a meal. He, therefore, calls sexual intercourse, bloodletting or the taking of a hot bath immediately after eating as an offense against one's health because they involve strenuous physical and emotional exercise. Finally, Maimonides enumerates a variety of ailments which occur in people who insufficiently or inadequately digest their food: heartburn, loose stools, impotence, insomnia, lethargy, depression, urinary retention, fever or inflammation of the kidneys, spleen, liver or joints.

Chapter six deals with the timing and number of meals one should eat. Maimonides suggests that healthy people should eat a single meal daily and that the elderly and/or debilitated and those convalescing from illness should consume small quantities at frequent intervals. One should only eat when the stomach is empty. The time to eat again is when the food has left the stomach, when there is no aftertaste from eructation and when one feels real appetite and salivates in the mouth — even then one should wait another half hour. Maimonides then recounts his personal eating habits. He used to eat only once in twenty four hours, except on the Sabbath. In the winter he drank a little wine, depending on the degree of cold, before going to bed. For Moslems to whom wine is prohibited, Maimonides suggests a fine honey drink.

Chapter seven deals with beverages. Excessive imbibition of wine is said to be injurious in that it makes the drinker feel heavy, affects his brain and hearing, gives rise to severe diseases and aggravates others such as asthma. However, a small quantity of wine during or after meals is useful in the diet of healthy people and an excellent cure for many disorders in that it aids digestion, increases natural body warmth and removes superfluities in the form of sweat and urine. Maimonides again offers a substitute for wine for Moslems to whom wine is forbidden: honeyed drink (i.e., mead) seasoned with spices. He also lists spices which stimulate urination: lentils, borax, mint, anise, mastic, muscat, nuts and nard. Recommendations regarding the drinking of water include the following: it should be sweet, clear and pure, boiled a little and drunk from a clean vessel after it cools down. The best time to drink water is about two hours after eating.

Chapter eight is concerned with rules of conduct regarding fresh air and psychic or emotional moods. Not only should air be fresh and clean but its temperature is important. On hot days, the air should be conditioned by spraying and sprinkling the floor with aromatic water, by flowers, heat abating leaves and draft. Conversely, on cold, rainy days, the air should be fumigated with perfumes which warm the body. Maimonides asserts that if a person is emotionally upset or mentally agitated, his physical well being suffers and eventually he becomes physically ill. This statement is perhaps an early description of psychosomatic medicine indicating that a deranged psyche can profoundly affect the somatic or physical well being of an individual. Conversely, continues Maimonides, gaiety and joy gladden the heart, and stimulate the blood and mental activity. Excessive indulgence in the pursuit of pleasure, however, is injurious to one's health. The avoidance of illnesses induced by such excesses is by conducting oneself according to ethical and moral principles.

In chapter nine Maimonides discusses constipation, urinary retention and other forms of retention of body superfluities. A variety of oral cathartic preparations and antidiarrheal concoctions are described. One should try to regulate one's bowels by maintaining a regular and normal diet. Very potent cathartics shoud be avoided. Numerous types of enemas to cleanse the stomach are listed. The conditions under which all these remedies are to be used are clearly enunciated. For example, vomiting is best effected when the patient is in a raised position, so that nothing remains in the stomach, Maimonides then describes a series of experiments that he conducted on himself to regulate his bowels. Finally, he posits that urine stimulation, bloodletting and purgation do not preserve health and should not be done on healthy people but reserved for cases of illness.

Chapter ten deals with the effects of sleeping, waking, bathing, massage and coitus on asthma. Sleeping immediately after meals is said to be harmful as is washing with cold water. Sleeping after bathing is efficacious. The bath water should be warm and contain some salt. Massaging the body upon awakening in the morning and before going to bed at night is highly recommended. Several types of massaging are described as are certain forms of exercise for the young and for the elderly. The final portion of this chapter is devoted to a discussion of coitus, an excess of which is injurious even to healthy people. A man who indulges excessively in coitus suffers from memory lapses and decline in mental capacity, faulty digestion and defective vision. Coitus soon after a bath or soon after physical exercise or bloodletting or at daybreak or when a person is hungry or fully satiated or seriously ill should be avoided.

In chapter eleven, Maimonides discusses simple medicinal therapy for asthma. He advises one to use an experienced and expert physician who develops a rational treatment plan and implements it. He counsels against the use of "empiricists who do not think scientifically" but who succeed or fail in treating patients purely by chance. He cites the following parable: a patient who puts his life in the hands of an experienced physician who is lacking in scientific training is like a mariner who places his trust in good luck, relying on the sea winds which sometimes blow in the direction desired by the mariner but which sometimes spell his doom. Maimonides is obviously cautioning against consultation with and treatment by medical quacks. In support of his position, he cites Galen and Hippocrates who assert that medicines should be compounded scientifically and logically according to the individual qualities of the patient. Specifically for asthma, Maimonides recommends enemas "to drain the thick juices", and aromatic herbs "to fortify the brain and dry out any humidity therein".

These should be employed once or twice a year. During an acute attack, chicken soup is advised if the patient is afebrile and sweetened barley porridge if the patient has fever. Should these be insufficient to allay the attack, an enema should be used. For the most severe cases, an emetic may be necessary. The patient should sleep as little as possible and in a sitting position. Excessive bathing and strenuous physical exercise should be avoided but light exercise may be beneficial.

Chapter twelve describes compound remedies for asthma in ascending order of potency, The mildest remedy is made from liquirita, althaea, fleabane and fennel boiled and strained into freshly made rosewater syrup. Maimonides endorses a remedy of Rhazes to clear the lungs of moisture, ease respiration and eliminate the cough: soak wheat bran overnight in hot water, filter and add sugar and almond oil; place on the fire until it resembles a julep and drink when lukewarm. A mild remedy of Galen for asthma consists of equal parts of seeded raisins and fenugreek cooked in clear water, sifted, and left standing for a prolonged period.More potent remedies of Galen are also described.

Maimonides cautions against the use of opiates except for severe cases of asthma. He details at some length the case of one of his patients who suffered from asthma, a young, thin, unmarried woman with a moderately warm constitution for whom he prepared a remedy containing numerous ingredients. His purpose was "To cleanse her lungs, fortify her brain and stop her catarrh". He states that no mention of this remedy is found in any of the medical texts written by ancient or modern physicians but that he had great success therewith. Maimonides again asserts that chicken soup assists in the expectoration and expulsion of pulmonary phlegm. He points out that Ibn Zuhr preferred powders to oily pastes for "fortifying the brain" in asthmatic patients. Various formulae for ointments, fumigations, enemas and purgatives are then described and their varying degrees of potency are cited. Most of these formulae were taught to Maimonides by "Western [i.e., Moroccan] Masters" and only a few are recorded in medical books. He concludes this chapter by stating that he only listed those remedies for asthma whose ingredients are easily available and whose preparation is simple.

The last and most important chapter of Maimonides' *Treatise on Asthma* is concerned with concise admonitions and aphorisms which he considered "useful to any man desirous of preserving his health [i.e., the patient] and administering to the sick [i.e., the physician]". The chapter begins as follows: "the first thing to consider... is the provision of fresh air, clean water and a healty diet." Fresh air is then described in some detail:

> "...city air is stagnant, turbid and thick, the natural result of its big buildings, narrow streets, the refuse of its inhabitants... one should at least choose for a residence on a wide-open site... living quarters are best located on an upper floor... and ample sunshine... toilets should be located as far as possible from living areas. The air should be kept dry at all times by sweet scents, fumication and drying agents. The concern for clean air is the foremost rule in preserving the health of one's body and soul..."

Healing of illness is said to be dependent not only upon the therapeutic measures prescribed by the physician but also the nature and constitution of the patient. In mild cases of illness, the physician should not interfere but allow nature to heal. If the physician should not interfere but allow nature to heal. If the physician errs and prescribes a therapy which is contrary to the course of nature, he may impede the cure or even aggravate the illness. Even if the physician prescribes correctly and even if the patient follows the prescription precisely, it is possible that cure will not be effected because nature may not cooperate. The same may happen to the farmer; he does everything that is expected of him yet the seeds bring forth no fruit if nature does not cooperate. Maimonides then quotes the famous aphorism of Rhazes who said:

> when the disease is stronger than the natural resistance of the patient medicine is of no use. When the patient's resistance is stronger than the disease, the physician is of no use. When the disease and the patients' resistance are equally balanced, the physician is needed to help tilt the balance in the patient's favor.

This rule of *primum non nocere* was already enunciated centuries earlier by Hippocrates who said that the physician should help the patient and not harm him. If one cannot help him, at least do not harm him. Maimonides then criticizes "famous physicians who commit grave errors on patients who later succumb..." Maimonides says he often observed a physician prescribe the use of a strong purgative for a patient who did not even need a mild one. Some physicians commit gross blunders, according to Maimonides, yet the patient survives; others commit seemingly small errors and the patient dies. Anyone with common sense should keep this in mind. The genuine physician is always beset with doubts whereas the charlatan thinks that everything is clear.

Maimonides cites Rhazes' aphorism which considers medicine to be an art, and Galen's assertion that "the medical art seems easy and simple to men of limited vision but how profound and far-reaching was this art in the eyes of a man like

Hippocrates". Maimonides makes reference to his *Commentary on the Aphorisms of Hippocrates*. He also quotes Aristotle who said that most people die of the remedies given them, a clear reference to iatrogenic desease. This observation, however, should not lead one to abandon appropriate remedies. Medicine is a science essential to man at all times and in all places, not only for the ill but also for the healthy. However, one should seek out and consult with expert physicians who have complete mastery of theoretical and practical knowledge. An unlearned physician should be avoided; if an expert physician is not available one should rely only on nature, confirming Hippocrates' assertion that "nature cures disease... she takes no orders from man... nature does all that is necessary...". Where a diagnosis is in doubt, it is best to rely on nature to cure the illness.

The humble Maimonides then addresses himself to the Sultan for whom he wrote his *Treatise on Asthma* saying:

> do not assume that I am the right person in whose hands you might place your body and soul for treatment. Heaven be my witness that I myself know well that I am one of those who are not perfect in this art [of medicine] and who shrink from it because it is enormously difficult to attain its vastness...

The chapter continues with the observation that therapeutic measures developed by practical experience are more frequently employed than those arrived at by theoretical reasoning. Maimonides again warns against the use of "experienced" quacks. The genuine physician has at his disposal not only his own experience but that of all physicians over many generations up to the time of Galen and Hippocrates as recorded in medical books. Another cardinal rule is that the physician should not treat the disease but the patient who is suffering from it.

The case of a young Moroccan patient who was wrongly treated and whose care was then taken over by one of Maimonides' teachers is cited in detail. Other cases of erroneous treatment with fatal outcome are also mentioned. Another case described in detail is the illness of the Sultan Amrael Muselmin in Marakesh, Morocco, treated by four of the greatest professors of medicine: Abu Ali Ibn Zuhr, Serapion, Abu Al Chassan Ibn Kammiel of Saragossa and Abu Ayub Ibn Almulin of Seville. The strong young Sultan recovered from his illness but later died, probably of an incorrect dosage of medicine. Maimonides investigated the circumstances surrounding the Sultan's death and comments thereon at some length. Maimonides expresses admiration for the fundamental rules of medical practice in Egypt and enumerates several reasons for his admiration. Finally, he lists the circumstances where more than one or two physicians should be consulted and where such multi-physician consultation should be avoided.

Chapter thirteen and the entire treatise end with the following prayer:

> May God the Gracious and Truthful guide us on the
> right path to our salvation in eternity. Praise be to God
> forever and ever.

Maimonides' medical genius is readily apparent in his *Treatise on Asthma*. His logical and systematic approach to the prevention, diagnosis, and treatment of illness is typical of all his medical and other writings. His allusion to psychosomatic medicine and his discussion of iatrogenic disease are far ahead of his time. His teachings that a bad physician is worse than none, that one should treat patients and not diseases, and that *primum non nocere*, among others, should be taken to heart by all students of medicine and medical practitioners of the present era. It is hoped that this essay describing Maimonides's *Treatise on Asthma* will stimulate the reader to read this important Maimonidean medical work in its entirety as well as his other nine medical books, all of which are now available in English.

MOSES MAIMONIDES' TREATISE ON ASTHMA

THUS SAID THE RABBI,
RABBENU MOSHE BEN MAIMON[1]
SERVANT OF THE LORD,
THE ISRAELITE FROM CORDOVA

INTRODUCTION

Our master, the honored nobleman — may the Lord prolong his life[2] — asked me[3] about this serious illness which he has and which is called *rinafli*[4] in other languages and *alrabu* in Arabic. He charged me with writing something about the foods which one should avoid and those which one should consume together with appropriate rules of conduct to follow which are beneficial for [patients with] this illness, as we have already clarified and as was also explained by the great physicians [of former times].

It is well known to physicians that this illness has many causes[5] and differs according to the different causes. Naturally, it is well known and clear to physicians that it is impossible to arrive at the proper methods of treatment for this illness without first examining the constitution of the patient in general and the constitution of each of his organs individually and certainly the constitution of the organ which is ailing and its partners in pain[6]. Then one should examine the fatness of the patient and his stoutness[7] or leanness which is also part of his constitution. Then one must consider his age[8] and his habits[9] and the time of the year and the weather at that time.

If my intent in this general treatise would have been to write about the details[10] of this illness including to whom it occurs and in what places it occurs and when it occurs and from what cause it occurs, it would be a very lengthy [treatise] and it would be necessary to provide an in-depth introduction to each section. Such is not the intent of this treatise because physicians have already written all that is necessary [to know] about this illness[11]. And this illness is not rare and its causes are not unknown[12] so that I should have to write a treatise about it. Furthermore, I have no miraculous cure[13] to report for which I would write a [special] treatise. Rather my intent in this treatise is only to fulfill the charge which our Master placed upon me — may the Lord heal him.

I already know from the testimony of others[14] and from what you[14a] have told me that the cause of this illness is a dripping from the brain[15] which occurs mostly in the autumn[16]; and the breathlessness and the discomfort do not abate day and night according to the length or brevity of the attack until the dripping ceases and until that which reaches the lung is absorbed[17] and the latter is cleansed. That is what I know about the cause of this illness. So, too, you told me that you had to take a loosening remedy[18] at least once or twice each year which would expel the phlegm and cleanse the lung and the brain[19]. Very often you take the loosening remedy during an attack and you become weak[20] as a result of it. I also know that you are approximately forty years of age and that your body [build] is intermediate between leanness and stoutness and your general constitution[21] is very nearly that of an intermediate type and that you tend a little toward heat and the constitution of your brain is hot. And I also know, because you told me, that hot winds harm you[22] and you cannot tolerate their odors. And hairs are intolerable to you[23] and you obtain relief by shaving your head[24] often. And you cannot tolerate covering your head or the wearing of a large turban[25]. And these [symptoms] point to [excessive] heat of the brain.

You already told me that the air of Alexandria is extremely detrimental to you and that whenever you fear the arrival of an attack [of asthma] you arrange to go to Egypt[26] because the air of Egypt is drier and calmer thus making it easier for you to tolerate that attack. Similarly, you told me that many physicians prescribed regimens for you which they thought appropriate according to each of their opinions, but all these [regimens] failed to eliminate the illness. Having made these introductory comments which are necessary for successful [treatment of asthma] by a physician who delves into this treatise and who finds therein particular rules or duplicative suggestions, I will begin to answer that which you asked of me.

In this treatise, it seems best, in my opinion, to write general chapters[27] which might prove useful to all people for the preservation of health and the prevention of the development of illnesses. [I will also describe] remedies for most illnesses. I gathered them[28] from the writings of Galen and others as much as I was able to remember them while I was composing this work and I cited them in the names of their authors in order to lend prestige to the efficacy of their words. At the end I will write about beneficial rules of a general nature in relation to the preservation of health and the healing of illnesses. The intent therein is to help people in general as much as possible so that the benefit of this entire treatise will accrue not only to my Master but also to others.[29] I thought it appropriate to divide [these health rules] into chapters to facilitate remembering them and so that the reader can rapidly find whatever subject he desires, with God's help:

The first chapter includes the best regimen of health in general.

The second chapter describes dietary measures[30] which one should follow or avoid in this illness.[31]

The third chapter mentions various types of foods which one should avoid or consume from among the easily available and commonly consumed foods.

The fourth chapter deals with the preparation of foods which are beneficial for this illness.

The fifth chapter deals with the quantity of food [that one should consume].

The sixth chapter deals with the times for eating meals.

The seventh chapter deals with beverages.

The eighth chapter deals with conduct concerning the air[32] and the movements of the soul.[33]

The ninth chapter deals with regimens for [body] emptying[34] and retention.

The tenth chapter deals with conduct regarding sleep and awakening and washing[35] and massaging and sexual intercourse.

The eleventh chapter describes therapeutic measures for this illness.

The twelfth chapter deals with the compounding of various drugs necessary for the various types of illness,[36] according to the intent of this treatise.

The thirteenth chapter is composed of passages few in number but of great help to all people in regard to the preservation of health and the cure of illnesses. These passages should be like commandments.[37]

Having divided [this treatise into] these chapters, I now begin[38] to elucidate all that which is contained in each chapter with brief explanations, with God's help.

THE FIRST CHAPTER
includes the best regimen of health in general.

1. It is important for whoever examines this treatise to know that for all established illnesses[39] which occur in attacks[40] such as podagra,[41] arthritis,[42] a stone,[43] asthma which is called *rinapli* in other languages, migraine which is an illness affecting half the head, and other illnesses resembling these,[44] cure is not known[45] or is difficult. Concerning each of these illnesses, if the patient follows a good [therapeutic] regimen and is familiar with it and is very careful to abstain from all that which he should abstain from and relies on all that which he should rely upon, he thereby at least prolongs the interval between two attacks and reduces the severity[46] of attacks and is more able to tolerate them. But if he neglects his regimen and indiscriminately[47] follows his lusts and usual habits, the interval between attacks is thereby shortened and the severity of attacks and the suffering[48] increase until the patient dies with extreme pain.

    Even if one of the organs is naturally weak from birth[49] and has not ceased receiving humors[50] because of its weakness, a good regimen diminishes the humors and thereby eases the patient's condition, whereas a bad regimen increases his humors and the severity of his attacks.

    We have already pointed out in this chapter the great efficacy which accrues from all good [conduct] in this art [of medicine]. And Galen made statements [on this matter] and these are his words. He said: that which confirms what we have said and absolutely proves it is the fact that there are[51] some people with weak organs in their bodies in whom coughing movements only occur once every six months or at even longer intervals. But if the weak organ was solely responsible for the illness, because of that weak organ, he would be constantly ill.[52] However, the cause of the illness is not always known and there is [often] another factor which plays a role in the development of this illness and which adds to it either quantatively or qualitatively.

2.   Says the author[53]: Galen has already explained and proven that the weak organs become diseased because of an excess of humors even if the latter are good ones or because of bad humors even if the latter are small in quantity. But if the humors are plentiful and their quality is bad, the damage is great. Galen also stated that he cured a large multitude of people of their illness if they exclusively followed a good regimen including regular exercises[54] for many years. Galen further stated that damage also occurs to one's moral qualities if one persists with bad habits[55] in relation to eating and drinking. But a good regimen can markedly improve one's moral virtues.[56] These are the beneficial rules which are extremely helpful and upon which one can rely[57], and which sick patients and healthy people should follow.

3.   It is already known that the regimen for all healthy and sick people has been arranged by physicians into seven subjects, six of which are indispensible and one of which is not indispensible.[58] The six indispensible subjects are the air[59] which surrounds us, what we should eat and drink, one's emotions,[60] bodily exercise[61] and physical rest which is opposite to it, sleeping and waking up, and evacuation and retention.[62] The subject which is not indispensible is that which only affects the body on occasion such as bathing[63] and massaging.

4.   Concerning sexual intercourse, not one of the ancient physicians established a regimen for the preservation of health. However, Hippocrates mentions it in the remedies for the sick because it is necessary to preserve the semen[64]

for [some patients with] bad constitutions. Mostly, however, a person uses [his semen] without any need[65]but solely out of lust. It, therefore, seems proper to include [sexual intercourse] in this [seventh] subject.

And I will further speak at great length or only briefly, according to my understanding, of items which relate to each of these seven subjects in this treatise.

THE SECOND CHAPTER
describes dietary measures which one should follow or avoid according to this illness.

1. It is appropriate to avoid any food which gives rise to a thick or sticky mixture [of humors] as well as a very large amount of food even if the latter is good food. And one should also avoid an excess of very rich food.[66] But it is appropriate to consume[67] food which is moderate[68] in quantity or even somewhat less and whose quality is such that it is not sticky or thick or is only a little bit sticky. The reason for this [regimen] is clear, that is to say if foods which are digested in the organs and the residue from the third digestion[69] is only a little, not sticky and not thick, its elimination is easy and it leaves the body through respiration[70] and perspiration. If somewhat more residue remains [after digestion], it can be easily eliminated through the openings of the body and is excreted with the feces and the urine and their like. But if the residues are many or sticky or thick, they cannot be easily eliminated nor excreted through the openings of the body and they wander through the organs and have difficulty being excreted from them. If the organs are extremely strong,

they resist the residues which then traverse into weaker organs and settle there and remain there and increase the damage.[71] And if the physician wishes to dilute them[72] there and to eliminate them, he has to resort to strong remedies or [to treat] for a long time or both, according to the thickness or stickiness or excess of the humor and according to the narrowness or wideness of the openings in that organ and according to the weakness or strength of the organ and that which surrounds it. This [inability to easily eliminate excess or faulty humors] is due to the fact that only a small amount of the humors change and only a small effect occurs even with the physician's [good] intentions because they do not leave the site where they are established. They[73] harm everything that comes into their path until they cause a serious occurrence which leads to the destruction of the organ and to the destruction of the entire body. Therefore, a fattening[74] [dietary] regimen is a sinful habit for everyone and, if pursued to the extreme, consitutes a great danger for some people. It is essential[75] that all the vessels and the openings be patent and the passageways completely cleared of obstruction and narrowness[76] so that the gasses[77] and humors can flee and so that the residues can emerge from them.

2.   And Galen made a statement and these are his words: It is important and most appropriate that the openings for the food[78] and[79] the passageways from the liver be patent and clean, not only in sick patients but also in healthy people. And in another chapter he states as follows: it is for this reason that I advise all people to avoid all foods which give rise to bad humors. Even a person who can digest them rapidly and easily should not endanger himself [by eating such foods] because after a certain time interval they will gather in the vessels and the latter cannot burn[80] extremely bad humors. And then, when the slightest insult

occurs to them which adds to the putrefaction [of humors], they putrefy and bad fevers develop as a result.

Says the author[81]: it is a very helpful rule[82] and most valuable advice for every person to abstain from fattening foods[83] in general. But in this illness[84] and for the man about whom we speak,[85], a fattening regimen destroys the body whereas a lightening regimen[86] is very beneficial as we have explained. However, it is also not appropriate to go to the latter extreme.[87] Rather, the body should be intermediate between fatness and leanness as we have mentioned. Similarly, it is appropriate to avoid all foods which generate gas and fill the head, and certainly if they are very hot [foods]. For weakness of the head[88] is increased by foods[89] which heat because the reason for the weakness is heat.

As Galen has explained, the strength of all organs deteriorates if they stray far from their intermediate condition irrespective of which quality they stray from. In addition, any organ which becomes hot attracts [residues] so that the brain does not become filled. The residues increase and settle in[90] the lungs as commonly happens in this illness. And the narrow and wide bronchial tubes which emanate from the trachea become filled and bathed with that humor.[91] And it is also appropriate that one avoid foods which are difficult to digest because whatever is digested with difficulty in the stomach remains there for a prolonged period of time until some of the gasses ascend to the brain and make it heavy and fill it and increase the weakness.

This is what I saw necessary [to cite] in this chapter according to [the intent of] this treatise.

THE THIRD CHAPTER

mentions various types of food which one should avoid or consume[92] from among the foods easily available and commonly consumed.

1. Galen has already explained that everything prepared from wheat flour which was extremely well sifted represents a food which contains fatness[93] and stickiness and is difficult to digest but is very nourishing. And its harmful effect does not dissipate unless it is made with[94] *darmak* flour;[95] and there should be recognizable leaven in the bread as well as salt; and it should be well kneaded and smoothed;[96] and it should be baked in an oven and it should be well digested.[97] For any bread that is prepared in this manner is better than that which can be prepared from whole grains.[98] After oven bread in excellence is furnace bread and after *darmak* flour in excellence is flour made from wheat which has not been soaked in water nor peeled and which has been lightly sifted so that all its bran[99] should not be lost; and it should be moderately ground.[100] For this type of flour, if kneaded as we have mentioned and baked as aforementioned, consitutes a good and pleasant food, easy to digest and intermediate in its nourishing effect. Anything made from wheat other than this is harmful to all people in general and to our Master[101] in particular. And I, therefore, need not warn you against those [foods] which are made from wheat such as *harifot*[102] or *chalkagi targis*,[103] nor against those [foods] which are cooked from flour such as rolled oats,[104] nor against those [products] where the dough is cooked such as noodles[105] which are called *eltariya* and their like,[106] nor from those [foods] which are mixed with oil or fried in it because these increase stickiness[107] and induce heat, such as pastries[108] mixed with oil and *koshkanim*[109] and pancakes. Similarly,

puff paste products[110] are extremely detrimental because they are unleavened and because of their stickiness and because they are poorly[111] baked. If in addition they are treated with cane sugar[112] and eaten with honey and fried, they are important causes of illnesses which develop in healthy people and even more so in sick patients who are attempting to correct their humors[113] and are attempting to remove the stickiness-[producing] ingredients from their foods. For in all these pastries[114] which are fattening foods, the oil adds to the stickiness in all cases, as we have mentioned. And if, in addition, one adds honey or cane sugar to them, they cause great harm to the liver which becomes more obstructed[115] because that taste becomes mixed in the liver and seizes much of it and reaches to the ends of the liver until it settles in the vessels and obstructs them. Know this matter and avoid it more than anything else one should avoid. And understand from all this that the flour from which one prepares semolina should be derived from the innermost grain[116] of the wheat and free[117] of any admixture.

2.   Galen said: anything prepared from wheat gives rise to thick humor which has difficulty in moving and obstructs the alimentary passages from the liver. And the spleen becomes hard and enlarges and stones are formed in the kidneys. And Galen also said that unleavened bread as it is is not appropriate and is not beneficial to anyone.[118]

3.   Says the author[119]: So, too, a person should avoid all the seeds which produce flatulence[120] such as beans,[121] peas,[122] haricot beans,[123] and chickpeas;[124] and those which fatten such as rice[125] and lentils; and everything which produces gasses in the head such as nuts; and everything which also increases heat such as leek,[126] onions and garlic. Similarly one should totally avoid fattening[127] meat such as that from cattle and goats and grown sheep[128] because

Galen asserts that these are worse than the meat of cattle.

4.   And it is well known that cheese is a fattening[129] food, and if it is old, is extremely detrimental. All the usual types of milk fill the head; therefore, do not consume them.[130] Similarly, all water fowl such as geese and duck are thick[131] and hard[132] and contain large amounts of harmful humors. It is appropriate for you to choose fowl meat which is not fat because such meat only has a little residue and is rapidly digested; [choose] also the *durag,*[133] the turtle dove and the partridge. The smaller fowl, — such as tiny birds, — the more efficacious they are for this illness; all the more so if they are roasted or prepared in a pan with barley soup. The soup of large chickens is an effective remedy for this illness. Although chicken egg yolks constitute an excellent food and certainly if they are soft boiled[134] and not cooked until they harden, I do not recommend their regular use because of their excess of humors. And ocean fish which have a young body and little fat and white meat and pleasant taste that can be separated to lessen their stickiness consitute a good food for you[135] because they are easily digested and have little residue. And river fish are not detrimental provided they come from a large river which has pure[136] water.

5.   So far, for this illness, I have spoken to you about fish with scales. Also widely recommended[137] for this illness are salty fish[138] with scales because of their tenderness and lightness.[139] However, one should not consume a lot of them so that they should not make the phlegm become sticky. And I also recommend that you consume the type of fish known as *muglas* and from the salted, clefted, smooth fish which contains little salt.[140] The latter is good if consumed once or twice a month.

6.   In any event, you should mostly eat the meat of small cattle[141] because it is commonly consumed and is easily

available. It is appropriate that you consume [meat] from a yearling or [a sheep] at the beginning of its second year and avoid one that has completed two years of life. And you should consume [meat] from sheep grazing in the field and not from those fattened in the manger[142] because the latter contain much residue, especially the fat ones. The meat of the female of this species is extremely detrimental to people in general and to you[143] in particular because of its stickiness, its total hardness [to digest] and its very large amount of residues. However, the legs[144] are devoid of humors but contain stickiness. In general, you should not consume meat from the male of this species except from the anterior half [of the animal[145]] and from that which is attached to bone such as the shoulder and the meat of ribs which are above the heart.

Beware of the fats in the abdomen because they are detrimental in general for all people because of their stickiness and their harm to digestion. They satisfy and reduce the desire to eat but, for this illness,[146] they are mostly destructive because of their moistening effect. And it is not proper that any food whatsoever should have much fat in it. Even if the [healthful] meat which we mentioned earlier should have a lot of fat on it, remove it and do not leave it with the meat except for that amount which makes the meat tasty.[147]

7. And know that meat of gazelles and deer and rabbits is good and highly recommended[148] for this illness although these are foods which are not beneficial.[149] Similarly the fat of rabbits is recommended for this illness. That which surpass all remedies for this illness — although they are bad foods — are fox meat, especially their lungs, and the meat of the wild hedgehog. These are extremely beneficial for this illness because they dry out the harmful substances and correct that which they can correct. Their lungs are particularly beneficial in this illness.

8.   Among the various types of vegetables recommended for this illness are the beet,[150] asparagus[151] — eventhough it may be difficult to digest — fennel,[152] parsley,[153] mint, mentastrum,[154] hyssop,[155] water cress[156] and radish.[157] All these, although bad foods,[158] are like remedies for this illness. However, moistening and cooling vegetables such as lettuce,[159] garden orach,[160] mallow,[161] gourd,[162] and their like are detrimental[163] for this illness and one should avoid them. The same applies to plants which have thick substances[164] such as colocassia,[165] rutabaga,[166] pastinaca,[167] cabbage,[168] aubergine,[169] and turnip.[170] All these should be avoided because their substance is thick and, although they contain liquid, they purge.[171] You should not consume them at all[172] because they accumulate the detrimental and thickening sustances of foods.

9.   Among the moist fruits some are juicy[173] such as watermelons, peaches,[174] apricots,[175] mulberries,[176] cucumbers,[177] and gherkins.[178] These are bad because liquifying fruits are all in general bad aliments for everyone and for those with this illness and especially those which we have enumerated. The same applies to green fruit[179] which refers to dates which have insufficiently ripened on the tree which should be eaten when juicy, thick and sticky; otherwise they produce headache. And the same applies to grapes which cause distention[180] in the organs of distention. Physicians assert that these [juicy fruits] fill the head and make digestion more difficult.[181] If one drinks a little of their juice in the morning when the stomach is empty and then eats a food with an acid taste, cooked with mint, it does no harm.[182] Fresh figs, however, should not be avoided but one should not constantly eat them because, although they cause distention, they do no harm if one consumes only a little of them since they rapidly leave the stomach. It is proper that one consume them, like other fruits, when the stomach is empty. Once their peel is removed, one can eat

as many as one desires if they are ripe. And if one consumes them with barley soup[183] or with vinegar or with salt into which are mixed rue,[184] mint,[185] and cumin,[186] it serves as a medicine and liquifies and purges.[187] And if it pleases you[188] to immerse the figs in one of these and to eat them, you should consume a little after you have completed the consumption of the figs. On that day, after the figs have passed from the stomach, your meal should be a light one such as small chickens or turtle doves or small birds cooked in vinegar or in lemon juice seasoned[189] with mint. If you then drink pomegranate juice, it is beneficial for the chest.

10. The sucking of quinces[190] after the meal is good but one should not use them excessively. All bound[191] foods such as quinces, *nabak*[192] and hemlock[193] are harmful for this illness. And raisins aid digestion[194] and soften the stool and alleviate the inflammation[195] of the anus, stomach and bronchi[196] but one should [first] discard their pits. The same applies to dried figs if one dipped them in grated and sifted anise.[197] And you should always complete [the meal] with pistachio nuts[198] and almonds, especially the bitter ones mixed with the sweet ones until their consumption becomes a habit[199] because they are an excellent remedy for this illness. They liquify[200] the humor,[201] cleanse the lungs[202] and assist in eliminating one's bad thoughts.[203] Similarly the fruit of the large cinnabar[204] is good in that it cleanses the lung especially if soaked in hot water; allow its waters to dry out and evaporate and then eat it. There is no harm in [eating] a small amount of hazelnuts. However, we mostly avoid walnuts because of the gasses they generate in the brain. And one should consume the dried kernels[205] of all these fruits with sugar and a little dried sweetening substance but the latter should not contain starch[206] or sesame.

THE FOURTH CHAPTER
*deals with the preparation[207] of foods
which are beneficial for this illness.*

1. I have described[208] the properties of the foods which should be avoided and those which should always be consumed by a patient suffering from this illness. I have also described their various types. Accordingly you can prepare various dishes from these aliments which are known to us and are widely used. Among them are [the following]: rue,[209] *barang*[210] [prepared] with beets, chicken meat or mutton, as we have previously recommended. And if one cooks the aliment with beans and the beans are not to one's liking, the soup of this dish or the water in which the beans were soaked is nevertheless beneficial.

2. Among these aliments is *sumkiya*[211] which is a food of the highest value and most pleasant taste. It serves as a remedy and is prepared as follows: boil[212] mutton or fowl meat; then roast it as other foods and seasonings that I will mention in this book are roasted; then remove the roasted meat and set it aside. After this, take raisins, remove their pips, and soak them in vinegar[213] for two hours. Then crush them in a stone mortar with peeled almonds equal to one quarter the amount of the raisins and pass [this mixture] through a sieve until the raisin peels are eliminated. Place this [sieved material] in the soup of the roasted meat until it is completely cooked. I saw this dish[214] in Egypt and I strongly recommended[215] its preparation because it liquifies and digests foods and warms to an intermediate degree. It tends to dryness[216] and opens [obstructions]. It is beneficial for all healthy people and even better for this illness.[217]

3. The advantage of this preparation is that the raisins fatten
    the liver and greatly benefit it; and they eliminate
    epigastric burning[218] and cleanse the lung and provide [the
    body] with calm and tranquility. And they[219] say that if one
    consumes them[220] excessively, they burn the blood. and the
    vinegar cuts up and liquifies and opens obstructions but it
    damages the liver and irritates it and whitens the blood[221]
    and harms the trachea and dries it out and thickens its
    mucus and thereby interferes[222] with coughing.[223] But
    when they[224] are mixed together, each ingredient shields
    against the damaging effect of the other and their
    combined beneficial effect remains, especially when this
    mixture is poured into chicken soup containing almond
    kernels. I have not seen a better preparation[225] than this
    one.

4. Similarly beneficial are *mashutz*[226] and *izarbag*[227] but one
    should use very little vinegar in them. Similarly, if it[228] is
    cooked with sugar and almonds or *kartami* which is wild
    saffron seed also known as *marzag,*[229] it is beneficial. So,
    too, almonds prepared with rose leaves are beneficial and
    one should use this [remedy] constantly in the winter
    time.[230] So, too, the dish prepared with honey whose froth
    has been removed or [prepared with] sugar and a little
    vinegar or lemons seasoned with spikenard[231] is an
    excellent composition. It is also appropriate in the winter
    time to eat a dish prepared from green fennel.[232] Its green
    leaves should be boiled and the cores[233] removed and
    boiled separately. After the boiling one adds chicken[234]
    which is not very fat. One covers the well roasted chicken
    meat with the leaves. It is called roasted because no water is
    added to the pot during the cooking except that which
    remains on the meat from when it was washed. One then
    leaves [the entire mixture] on the fire until its cooking is
    completed. And if one takes the shoots of the fennel after
    they have grown and multiplied and peels them and cuts

them up into seasoning and cooks with them as we have described, the resultant dish is beneficial and helpful to liquify [the phlegm]. This dish is known to us in the West, is commonly used and is extremely beneficial. Similarly, if one prepares the dish which is called *mamerzig*[235] and one adds to its soup one quarter of all these [aforementioned] things, and some barley gruel,[236] and a little of each of these[237] but not too spicy, [it is beneficial]. One leaves it until its cooking is completed. This dish has a pleasant taste and is easy to digest.

5.   Among the foods [popularly] used by the people of Egypt is bread salted with vinegar and honey whose froth has been removed or with vinegar and salt or with barley gruel. It is recommended that it always be on the table, especially during the winter season.

6.   One should dip a few pieces of bread[238] into the juice[239] of the *askil*.[240] Similarly, one should dip it a few times in mustard. We, in Spain, prepare the mustard as follows: one takes a *kav*[241] of *Shami* mustard,[242] soaks it in hot water overnight and pours off the water. The mustard is then placed in a stone mortar together with clean absorbent cotton so that it remains in place and does not fly out during the pounding. And it should be finely pulverized with strong vinegar. Then one adds a good quality sweet olive oil drop by drop[243] until the *kav* [of the mustard] has absorbed very well a *litre* of the good oil. Then one stirs it with white vinegar.[244] Then one takes a *litre* of peeled sweet almonds and pounds them until they resemble marrow and one also mixes them with the vinegar in which the mustard was stirred and strains the entire mixture through a linen cloth or a sieve until it develops the characteristics and appearance of milk so that it is undistinguishable [from milk] except in its taste. This [mustard preparation] is extremely helpful to digestion, loosens the phlegm, softens the stomach [contents],

liquifies the stickiness of the humors and does not excessively warm.

7. Know that remedies[245] which warm and dry [the body] are extremely harmful for this illness, especially for the consitution which we have mentioned[246] because they thicken the humors and have a fattening effect and they harden and congeal that which does not contain fat. I pay close attention to all this[247] so that your[248] foods should not contain the taste of spices[249] nor of those things which excessively warm as we commonly do in most of these countries.[250] Therefore, to the above-mentioned preparation, one should add half an ounce of pepper, two ounces each of cabbage stalks and cauliflower,[251] half an ounce of ginger, three *zuzim* of spikenard,[252] two *zuzim* of pistachio[253] and six ounces of dry coriander.[254] Pulverize all these and add an amount thereof to the food sufficient to season it but without it producing a warming effect.[255] However, foods prepared with vinegar are not harmful if, to that which we have already mentioned, one adds two ounces each of ginger,[256] aromatic cloves blossoms[257] and cedar leaves.[258] Indeed, they facilitate the softening[259] and fragmentation [of food] together with the vinegar. And one should follow the local custom concerning all foods into which are added certain ingredients and one should not omit any because such [foods] facilitate digestion[260] and soften and do not excessively warm [the body].

8. However, all sorts of sweets[261] which contain starch of even only a minute amount of wheat such as *chavitza*[262] and *kariah*[263] which is a type of Egyptian cake and their like, are bad. All these are extremely difficult [to digest] and cause constipation.[264] I have already mentioned in regard to fruits that one should consume dried sweet ones as well as the pine fruit coated with *panid*[265] just as one coats the pistachio or dips it [into salt water].

THE FIFTH CHAPTER
deals with the quantity of food
[that one should consume].

1. After having discussed the quality [of food to be
    consumed] it is appropriate to explain its [proper] quantity.
    The latter varies with the life rules of individual people.
    There are some people who have a large stomach and
    strong digestion and can tolerate a large amount of food.
    There are others who have a small stomach and weak
    digestion by nature and can only tolerate a small amount
    [of food]. It is known that the art of medicine takes these
    facts into account.[266] It is appropriate that every person
    should measure his food intake at a time that he is healthy
    and know that amount which, if consumed in the spring-
    time, can be easily tolerated and well digested. And the rule
    is that he should consume that amount; and he should
    reduce that amount when the heat increases a little[267] and
    increase [his food intake] at times when it becomes a little
    colder.[268] The main principle in this matter is to avoid
    satiation that leads to the distention of the abdomen more
    than the natural amount. For the activities of any organ
    that distends become obligatorily perturbed because
    distention[269] is a type of separation of attached parts. And
    if the stomach distends more than its natural size, its
    functions[270] weaken and it can no longer press the food
    which becomes heavy on it and loathsome to the point that
    it produces a craving for water in the absence of thirst.
    [This craving is] to neutralize the food[271] and to alleviate
    the heaviness by mixing it[272] with water. This is [the reason
    for] the drinking of large amounts of water after satiation.

2. Physicians have already fixed appropriate limits in this
    matter, that is to say, a person should stop eating[273] before
    food becomes loathsome to him,[274] preferably at a time

when most of his lust for food has been satisfied and when only a little desire [for food] remains. If living creatures such as horses, donkeys and camels who have no rules[275] in regard to the quantity [of food consumed] yet measure their intake and do not eat without limit,[276] how can a person not measure his food intake and eat according to his lust and not according to what he can tolerate to the point that the food sticks in his throat?[277]

3. And I have observed a few gluttons who sometimes eructate and return the food to their mouths like ruminating animals. And this is one of the major reasons for the causation of many illnesses because good food — even the best of all foods —, if consumed to excess, necessarily interferes with digestion and gives rise to bad humors which are the causes of very acute illnesses. Galen has already mentioned that such [conduct leading to acute illnesses] can produce death in one day if [food consumption is extremely] excessive and if not so excessive can cause death in two or three days or [simply] make the person ill. He may also suffer from constant eructation[278] which is one of the well-known occurrences as well as heartburn[279] which leads to fainting.[280] It is not our intent in this chapter to cite remedies for the different stomach ailments. Rather, the intent is to [have you] be on guard and therefore I describe the enormity of the harm [of gluttony] so that one can avoid it.

4. And physicians have already recommended[281] that one not eat many foods at a single meal and they recommend that one eat a single dish per meal. The reason they cite is the varying digestibility [of differing foods]. Since there is only one stomach, if different foods are contained therein, humors are formed which of necessity either hinder or improve the digestion. Best for digestion is a single food. They have also said that this is so [282] because then one need

not be concerned with the sequence of foods [consumed] because food can impede[283] digestion in many ways. It can impede [digestion] because of its quality or because of the quantity [consumed] as we have mentioned or because of their order since one should first consume heavy[284] and then light[285] foods, according to some opinions. But Galen states that one should first consume the light and then the heavy [food]. Similarly, one should first consume that which loosens[286] and then that which is astringent,[287] according to some opinions. If one consumes only a single food, one does not have to be concerned about this sequence which we just mentioned. And I believe[288] that this regimen[289] has a great advantage over one with two [foods] because multiple foods increase a person's appetite which increases[290] with each food consumed.[291] A single food curbs the appetite so that one does not eat thereof more than is necessary, unless one is dealing with[292] an exceptionally gluttonous person. In any event, a single food is less nourishing than many foods but it is recommended[293] to preserve one's health that one eat little so as not to attain satiation.

5.   Hippocrates spoke and the following are his words: the preservation of health consists of the guarding against satiation and the shunning of laziness and indolence. Galen already cited[294] a useful precept in this matter which I believe deserves[295] to be mentioned, and here are his words: Galen said that too much rest is bad for the preservation of health whereas[296] moderate exercise is greatly beneficial. This means that a person does not become ill if he is certain that he will never develop bad digestion and if he does not exercise excessively[297] after his meal. This is so because just as exercise before a meal is better then anything else[298] for the preservation of one's health, exercise after a meal is more harmful than anything

else because the food leaves the stomach and spreads throughout the body before it is digested and many chymes accumulate in the [blood] vessels. These [chymes] have the tendency to give rise to various illnesses unless they are dissolved beforehand such as by strenuous exercise or digested and converted to blood through the force of the liver and the vessels.

6.   Says the author:[299] resting after a meal is of great value. Therefore, it follows[300] that taking a bath,[301] sexual intercourse and bloodletting after eating constitute a great offense[302] because all these are exercises. Only rest is recommended after a meal. Also pay attention to the degree of benefit and be on guard against bad digestion because this is undoubtedly a cause of dyspepsia. Galen already enumerated [such cases] in his book of occurrences and stated as follows: each of these [symptoms] apparently[303] occurs to one whose food is not digested, and all these symptoms[304] develop in him. For sometimes one of these symptoms or many of them develop in one person according to the different natures [of people], their age, body dispositions and the different types of harmful foods [consumed]. And the symptoms which he mentions that develop as a result of bad digestion are the following: swelling[305] or burning[306] or weakness of the stools[307] or excessive stools[308] or feebleness[309] or loss of appetite or insomnia or epigastric pain or confusion and mental disorientation[310] or lethargy or melancholy[311] and the like, and pain in the *kolon* which means pains in the intestines or retention[312] or pain in the kidneys[313] or spleen or pain in the liver[314] or pain in the joints[315] or a general disturbance of the body[316] or shaking of the body[317] or fever.

7.   Says the author:[318] it is appropriate for intelligent healthy people to [carefully] consider and reflect whether a tasty food is beneficial enough to counter all the aforementioned

side effects mentioned by Galen. The way to avoid them is to eat a single good food and not to fill oneself therewith and not to exercise thereafter as mentioned earlier. If this preventive measure is an obligation for healthy people all the more so is it an obligation for those who already suffer from the enumerated ailments and especially for someone in whom one of the major organs[319] is naturally weak or in whom the ailments have already developed. [For all these] it is proper to become firmly accustomed to follow the best alimentary regimen whose types and modalities we have already mentioned.

THE SIXTH CHAPTER
deals with the times for eating meals.

1. Peoples' customs in this regard vary. Most eat in the morning and in the evening but there are others who eat three times a day and a small number who eat only once a day. I will ignore[320] your[321] custom in this matter. The general principle to which one should adhere is that healthy, vigorous people can consume all that they need at one time. However, if weak people such as the elderly and those convalescing from illness eat their entire nourishment at one time, they commit a great offense [against their health]. Rather, they should divide their food according to their weakness so as not to decrease their strength and extinguish their fundamental warmth.

2. In regard to the [alimentary] regimens for the elderly, Galen spoke the following words: I say that the best advice[322] for them is that when one's strength is weak one should feed the body with small amounts [of nourishment] at short intervals.[323] But when one's strength is forceful, one should feed [the body] a lot but at long intervals.[324]

3. Says the author:[325] this subject is repeated many times in his[326] books. The main point of his words — however one examines them[327] — is that one should not eat one meal after another; rather one should only eat when the stomach is empty,[328] not like the merchants who fix a certain time of day at a cerain known hour which never changes as if the meal was an obligatory prayer. But the proper thing to do is to eat only when the stomach is empty.[329] This [time] varies according to what food one eats and according to the length or brevity of the day and according to external circumstances. The lapse of time after which one can eat again is when the first food has already left the stomach and its taste does not remain if one eructates and the true desire for food has been reawakened and the saliva has finished flowing to the mouth. After all this, he should wait approximately another half hour. They say that no person should wait more than two hours and we determine [the time] according to the fatness or leanness of the body, the large or small amount of its humors and their warming or cooling effects.[330] A lean person whose humors are sparse and warming[331] should wait half an hour[332] and then eat. A person with the opposite characteristics should wait two hours. This is the criterion[333] of emptiness of the stomach that we have mentioned. One should not rely solely on hunger[334] because people with stomach ailments[335] often have a false [sensation of] hunger from the bad humors which are malignant and which cause pain at the mouth of the stomach.

We have already explained that a person whose custom is to eat in the morning and in the evening should, in the wintertime,[336] eat during the second or third hour of the day, depending upon the length of the night and his digestive power. During the summer,[337] he should eat during the fifth hour of the day and then his stomach empties [easily]. So too the time for eating in the evening is earlier or later[338] according to [the criteria] we have mentioned. And know that those who eat only once a day may sometimes during certain nights of the winter[339] awaken at the beginning of the night and their stomachs are [already] empty. It also sometimes happens that a person eats his meal before his customary time [especially] when the days are long and, when bedtime arrives, his stomach is [already] empty. These occurrences are quite frequent.[340]

4.   I have already observed and confirmed by personal experience[341] that if I eat bread, even only a little, I am harmed because of the change in my habit and my digestion is impaired. And if I fall asleep while the stomach is empty, humors prevail and the stomach fills with bad humors which are drawn to it as happens to those who fast. I, therefore, saw fit to subjugate my stomach[342] with tasty foods that are easy to digest. And sometimes I drink chicken soup and then fall asleep. And sometimes I roll[343] five or six eggs and eat their yolks together with a little cane sugar and salt. And sometimes I eat peanuts and raisins without their pips or [dried] raisins and almonds which are sugar coated and I drink a beverage containing sugar and honey — whichever one is available. But in the rainy season[344] I drink [several] glasses of wine depending on the coldness of the season and because in general one should not go to bed hungry unless one has agreeable humors which are unripe but which [the stomach] can cook.

5.   And I advise your Highness to follow all the aforementioned but instead of glasses of wine in the winter,[345] drink instead between a third and a half *litre* of sweetened honey. I have found this regimen to be extremely beneficial.

THE SEVENTH CHAPTER
deals with beverages.

1. Having discussed the proper alimentary regimen which one should follow, [we will now describe] a regimen regarding beverages, although most of this regimen does not apply to Moslems[346] because wine is prohibited to them. It concerns a type of wine which is prepared by boiling and mixing [with certain ingredients] and which is forbidden to most people. The Almighty has already saved your Highness from this and there is, therefore, no need to warn you to be on guard against it. Although all wines fill the head and harm the brain and warm it and give rise to serious and grave[347] illnesses and are also harmful for this illness,[348] it is the large quantity imbibed which produces these effects, and certainly drunkenness [is harmful]. However, a small amount of wine such as three or four glasses [imbibed] at the time the food is being digested and leaving the stomach is of benefit for the preservation of the health of human beings and an excellent remedy for most illnesses. Among its benefits are that it ameliorates digestion, increases and augments natural body warmth[349] and eliminates the superfluities in the sweat and in the urine. There is no benefit, however, in describing the advantage of something from which one cannot derive benefit.[350]

    In general, if a person drinks a little [wine] at the appropriate time, it is an important cause of the amelioration of the body and soul in all respects and especially in regard to the elderly, as we have explained, for they have no other way to manage without it. However, large amounts [of wine] destroy[351] the soul and the body of all people of all ages from the day of their birth to the day of their death.

2.   And since [wine] in large or in small quantities is prohibited to Moslems, physicians have attempted to find ways of preparing a substitute such as a honey beverage[352] which is seasoned and which resembles wine in most of its benefits except for the gladdening of the soul, but it removes the excessive gaseous wastes. And I will describe a recipe thereof for your Highness which I saw prepared by the elders and which has excellent effects when compared [to wine].[353] And I will add thereto some spices which are suitable for everybody and also for your Highness for they stimulate urination.[354]

Take half a *kav* of lentils,[355] — the black ones are most preferred — , wash them from their dust and soak them in five Egyptian *litres* of clear water for one night. In the morning, cook them until their strength leaves[356] but do not wait for the [complete] cooking of the lentils. Pass the water through a strainer into a *litre* of high quality[357] white honey, let it simmer on a small[358] fire and constantly[359] remove the froth [as it forms]. After the froth has been [totally] removed add half an ounce of oxtongue,[360] three stalks of mint[361] and spices and aromatics according to the age and consitution and according to the quality of the organs [of the patient].

It is my opinion[362] that it is proper for you according to your illness and, according to what I know of the constitution of your organs, to add to the lentils, while they are soaking, half an ounce of *pilsia*[363] which is called *kuzbarat albir* in Arabic and *Capilli veneris* in Latin. After having removed the froth, one should add anise[364] to this beverage. Also add two *zuzim* of cane,[365] half a *zuz* each of crushed ginger, mastic,[366] muscat and spikenard,[367] and one quarter *zuz* of saffron.[368] Squeeze all this with a spoon continuously[369] until it develops the characteristic of a liquid such as the limpidity of julep syrup.[370] Then remove it from the fire. One should not prepare more than a *litre* thereof at one time for if it stays for a long time it deteriorates and spoils[371] because of its weak quality. It is much better if it does not have to be diluted[372] with water. However, if one prepares it to have the quality of a beverage and places it in a glass and when needed dilutes it with water and drinks it, it lacks its beneficial effects. And if one needs it because one is leaving on a journey, one should dilute it with cold water [in the summer] and with hot water in the wintertime but not drink it at the time it is diluted but only later, after approximately one hour when it is well diluted. It is also my opinion that one should add a quantity[373] of mentastrum[374] which is water mint or increase the amount of mint to assist expectoration and to cleans the chest and the lungs of superfluities.

3. It is already known to most people that if water is imbibed together with food[375] it counteracts it and interposes[376] between the stomach and the food floats and impedes digestion. But if this custom of yours[377] is tolerable to you, at least drink as little as possible and delay it as much as possible. The best time to drink water is two hours after a meal. And it is proper to select sweet, clear and light water, free from any odor,[378] and which was drawn [fresh] on that day from flowing waters.[379] And one should boil the water a little, then let it cool and then drink it, for this [procedure] removes most of its harm and corrects most of the damages caused by its type.[380] And if one adds a small amount of liquorice[381] while the water is boiling a little so as not to produce a change in its taste, and adds muscat[382] sufficient to impart its taste and aroma, and boils these in a new pot for one hour, this water is the very best for all healthy people in summer and winter. It strengthens all the internal organs and ameliorates the stomach. Even a small amount has great utility. For someone suffering from any

ailment, this water alleviates his [discomfort] depending on the ailment.

And know that the drinking of tepid water, that is to say water in which the coolness is not recognizable is extremely detrimental to the digestion of all people. It weakens the lining of the stomach and even a lot does not quench one's thirst. On the other hand, cold water which does not frighten a person because of its marked coldness, and if it is not ice cold, is the choicest type of water and should be imbibed when one is thirsty and especially by people with a warm constitution.

4.   Physicians have already recommended[383] that even of this excellent water one should only drink a moderate amount and not excessively. They also said that it ameliorates digestion, adapts[384] the body of the stomach to the food, stimulates[385] the appetite and strengthens it, improves one's appearance,[386] prevents the development of fevers and acute[387] illnesses, prevents burning of the heart[388] and the stomach and putrefaction of blood in the vessels.[389] Even a little quenches thirst.

Tepid water produces the opposite of these effects and is a cause of bodily weakness, diminution of one's constitution and the beginning of asthenia.[390] Therefore, they said that there are many nations [the people of] which drink warm water, that is to say which is not cold, who have a yellow appearance and are pale and thin, susceptible to diseases of the spleen and liver, who have weak appetites, are lacking in fat and brightness [of expression] and joyfulness because their blood is bad and susceptible to diseases and inflammations[391] and infections.[392] Therefore, one should be extremely careful to avoid it.

5. Having completed the regimens concerning food and beverages, we will move to regimens concerning bodily exercise and rest. We will discuss the remainder of the seven topics[393] according to the intent of this treatise.

THE EIGHTH CHAPTER
deals with conduct concerning the air and the movements of the soul.[394]

1. It is known that one should regulate the air[395] and improve it and keep it free of impurities[396] for all healthy people. But for sick people, the air should counteract the illness. The same applies to situations which deviate from the middle course, that is to say on hot days one should regulate the air by pouring scented water[397] on the ground, by flowers and cooling leaves[398] and by [provoking] air flow.[399] Similarly, to warm [the air] on rainy[400] days, one should use perfumes which stimulate [body] heat and fire and herbs which dry [the air]. However, cold and humid air is extremely harmful to you.[401] And you should also be careful to avoid cooling or warming drippings[402] as much as possible.

2. Concerning one's emotions,[403] their importance is known, that is to say we observe that different types of mental anguish and mental distress[404] and weakness of mental faculties and natural vital functions reach the point that one's appetite for food is abolished from anguish and fear and grief and distress. For if [such] a person tries to raise his voice, he cannot do so because his mental distress weakens his respiratory organs which he cannot use[405] properly. And because of the gaseous excesses, he is unable to stand erect to inhale the air. He also does not have

sufficient strength to lift[406] his organs. If this condition
persists, he undoubtedly becomes ill and if it becomes
prolonged, he dies. These facts are well known and we do
not have to discuss them at great length.

And rejoicing and happiness have the opposite effect [in
that] they gladden the heart,[407] [promote] the movement of
the blood and the spirit, and the functions of the organs are
observed to be at their very best. But if one exaggerates this
[emotion] and greatly indulges in [activities of] pleasure as
do the simpletons who are lacking in intellect, one becomes
ill and may even die because the soul is destroyed and
corrupted and leaves [the body], and the heart becomes
cold and the person dies.

3.   And the therapy of these two types of emotional states and
their prevention[408] does not consist solely of foods[409] and
medicines, nor [is it in the province of] a physician who
engages in medical therapeutics. Rather, the therapy of
such affections depends upon other skills[410] such as the
virtues of philosophers[411] or the interpretations of the wise
and moral and ethical teachings. There is no doubt that
these [psychological methods] are of greater benefit[412] to
the patient [than standard medical therapy] and help
prevent him from developing [emotional illnesses] through
the interpretations of the wise who understand the nature
[of these illnesses] and the regimen necessary to preserve
one's existence in the world and [avoid] this harm. So too
philosophical virtues remove a person from [emotional]
states[413] so that he does not feel sluggish all alone nor
pleasure-seeking   like   animals   as   occurs   to   the
multitudes.[414] Rather, his emotions[415] are influenced, as
appropriate, by human counsel, not by physical activities
except for courage and cowardliness[416] and their like. So
too with moral and ethical teachings; the world and that
which is contained therein looks light in one's eyes as does

one's perception of prosperity or failure because both of these do not exist. One should not think [too much] thereof nor take comfort therein because, although they are important to us or appear in the forefront of our thinking, in reality if one delves into [this matter] it is all pleasantry[417] and sarcasm which vanish like the night.[418]

4. I have mentioned all these things although they are not part of the intent of this treatise because, in my opinion, they may help provide you[418a] with true and lasting prosperity and spare you from suffering.[419] For you are greatly grieved and in great distress[420] and this illness cannot be properly treated by a dietary regimen[421] nor totally cured by medical remedies. A person such as you should be careful and follow in the footsteps of the Sages and the prophets, to reject the benefit of the pain of the deceased[422] and to constrain one's nature to follow the laws of the Almighty in this matter and to occupy oneself with that which is useful and to set aside that which is not useful. And may the Lord show us the path of truth.

THE NINTH CHAPTER
deals with regimens for retention and evacuation.[423]

1. Among the best regimens for all people, especially for someone in whose body humors have accumulated[424] is for the stools to be always soft[425] or nearly soft. If they are sometimes hard[426] and this condition persists for some time, he becomes weak.[427] Ibn Zuhr[428] has already recommended the following regimen for soft stools:

dissolve ten *zuzim* of Indian date[429] in sufficient warm water to cover them and then soak therein three quarters of a *zuz* of crushed rhubarb[430] for twenty four hours, and make it into a clear beverage by adding an ounce of lemon peel juice.

2.   Says the author:[431] I recommend this [recipe of Ibn Zuhr] for someone whose humors are thin and for young people and for [people living in] hot climates. However, for someone whose humors are thick and sticky and for the elderly and especially for those suffering from the illness for which I composed this treatise, it is best to use the remedy mentioned by Galen which is prepared from the hearts of dried figs, the hearts of *kotan*[432] and raisins and the small fruits of the dogwood.[433] The manner of its preparation is to take five *zuzim* of safflower hearts,[434] one eighth of a *zuz* of table salt[434a] and twenty *zuzim* of the hearts of dried figs. Take all these and pulverize them in a stone or wooden mortar until it becomes a compact mass[435] and consume it with a mouthful of warm water because this [remedy] is extremely beneficial as was stated by Galen.

Another remedy[436] is to crush the small fruits of the dogwood[437] and strain them through a sieve with two ounces of bees' honey. This remedy softens [the stools] very well. Similarly, if one swallows approximately [the volume of] one nut of radish juice,[438] it softens[439] without harm, cleanses all the internal organs and liquifies that which is within them referring to the liver, spleen, kidneys, urinary bladder and lungs. One should take this remedy repeatedly.[440]

3.   Says the author: the same [laxative effect] occurs with beets[441] seasoned with barley gruel and much olive oil; its liquid[442] should not be discarded.[443] The same applies to the

concoction[444] well known in Egypt which is prepared with lemon juice and safflower seeds and beets. It is a good preparation for softening of the stools for most people. Similarly, honey water softens the stools. If it is boiled with sebesten[445] and acacia[446] and then strained over sugar and oil of sweet almonds, it softens the stools and facilitates the expulsion of wastes. One should select from among these [laxative remedies] those which are appropriate according to the characteristics of the body and [the patient's] age and the seasons of the year.

4.   But if the stools are looser than normal[447] and this persists for two or three days, one should reduce one's food intake and consume some of the commonly-used astringent foods such as the sumac[448] and unripe grapes[449] and raisins prepared with dried raisins including their kernels and pomegranates with beet ribs. Cook all these in quinces and rose water.

5.   In general, one should regulate one's stools[450] with customary foods and only imbibe a little of the customary beverages such as apple juice, but a lot of quince juice and other astringent[451] potions. And one should consume of these that which is available according to the season and also according to one's age. In regard to the quantity of these items [to be consumed], one does not need to consult a medical specialist nor need one be careful about the amounts because this matter is well known to most intelligent people in most lands where medicine is practiced.[452] However, one should be extremely careful and not take lightly for a moment nor undertake purgation with powerful medicines which provoke spasms except with the advice of a skilled physician. [Examples of such strong purgatives are]: colocynth *turbeed*,[453] scammony,[454] and their like. It is especially for the elderly that Galen

very strongly warned against the use of such drastic purgatives. Similarly, to stop diarrhea, one should not use strong [styptic] medications except upon the advice of a skilled physician who takes into account the circumstances of the illness.

6.   The emptying [of the intestines] by an enema[455] for the preservation of health and for the cure of illness is one of the best remedies, and its utility is exceedingly great because it empties [the body] of humors. [Even] if the enema contains astringent substances, it does no harm to the vital organs and does not provoke severe pains as do purgative medications. A person can rely on them[456] and their outcome is good. If the intent of the enema is only to loosen [the stool] and to evacuate the hard wastes, the enema serves as an excellent treatment for the maintenance of health and it is not necessary to treat with any [purgative] potions or their like because they also weaken the lining of the stomach[457] and provoke vomiting as do most laxative remedies [which are swallowed] during the meal.

In his book *On Clysters*, Galen mentions a number of remedies which are beneficial for the preservation of health if the stools are hard and dry and difficult to evacuate. These [remedies] are the following: [take] two ounces of honey, half a *litre* of water, an ounce of good quality olive oil and one *zuz* of *natron*;[458] heat all these and use as an enema. If you wish to treat dried wastes or to reduce their [quantity], add more oil. And if you wish to eliminate sticky mucus, increase the amount of honey and *natron*.

7.   Another [remedy] is to take half a *litre* of beet juice and two ounces of good quality olive oil; warm these and use as an enema. Another [remedy] is to take wheat bran[359] and

soak it in water so that it is [totally] covered; cook until one third of the water evaporates, pass it through a strainer, so that it becomes thick, place oil thereon and use this as an enema; this [remedy] is useful to evacuate dried wastes. These three enema recipes are preparations [cited] by Galen and I find them extremely good.

Similarly, enemas made with the sap of linseed or fenugreek[460] or both with oil and chicken fat and beets[461] constitute excellent preparations which evacuate wastes when there is constipation and which do not irritate or produce pain. For the elderly, if one also adds thereto a little honey or honey cake[462] [by mouth], it is beneficial, and this too is recommended by Galen.

8. Galen has already mentioned that an enema with the sap of linseed is beneficial for patients with consumption[463] because it calms the [bad] humors. And know that the regular[464] use of enemas cleanses the brain very well, empties the intestines, delays aging, improves the digestions,[465] and prevents many illnesses because they cleanse from below and wash the upper organs so that they find paved straight paths through which to expel the superfluities, — the same paths through which nature expels superfluities; and all that we have just mentioned is thus confirmed.

9. Know that there is nothing more harmful to the preservation of health and in the provocation of disease than the retention of the two [main] superfluities of nature.[466] Galen has already explained that the feces become entangled within the pneuma and damage all the humors because of the gasses[467] which ascend into the brain; and feces disperse all the pneumas and are the cause of the beginning of putrefaction and loss of digestion and the onset of severe diseases. The same [abnormalities]

develop from retention of urine. We have only mentioned but a few of these detriments. Therefore, one should be extremely careful in this matter.

10. Vomiting, however, is truly necessary for the preservation of health[468] of all people and should be used in the treatment of illnesses. Its therapeutic application for this illness[469] has been verified. One should, therefore, not eliminate vomiting from one's regimen of health except someone who is not accustomed to it or someone who finds it extremely difficult or someone who has a disease in his brain or his eyes. In my opinion, the reason why vomiting is necessary for the preservation of health is that, of necessity, superfluities develop in the stomach and intestines; the nature of phlegm is to be sticky and if this superfluity remains without being digested by these first [organs], — that is to say the stomach and the intestines, — it becomes interposed between the food and the body of the stomach and the intestines, and impedes digestion and some of the foods are lost. However, the intestines have been provided with a superior Divine Providence[470] in that the yellow bile brings the superfluity to them and cleanses that phlegm and liquifies it and constantly cleanses the intestines therefrom. It is impossible that even a minute amount of bile should enter the stomach because that would cause great detriments as enumerated by Galen. We rely on the craftiness of a person to cleanse his stomach through vomiting.

11. Galen expressed himself as follows:[471] the cleansing of the stomach can be accomplished easily. The ancient physicians correctly stated that part of the regimen for the preservation of health is to induce vomiting after a meal once a month. Some are of the opinion that one should cleanse [the stomach by vomiting] twice [a month]. But all

are of the opinion that before the vomiting one should eat
some foods which have a sharp taste and which have the
power to liquify and to cleanse. This is done to eliminate[472]
all the phlegm that is in the stomach without causing harm
to the body from the nausea generated by these [foods]
because all cleansing and sharp foods give rise to yellow
bile and all are bad foods.[473]

12. Says the author: one observes many people who fondly
desire detrimental sharp foods[474] such as salted cheese, fish
brine, and meat sauce, or putrefying foods such as
kamka[475], garlic,[476] various types of congealed milk,[477]
radish, onion, and their like. The reason for all this is that
phlegm gathers in the stomach over many days and a
person develops the desire for something that can
disintegrate and liquify [phlegms]. But if the stomach is
clean through vomiting, as mentioned by Galen, or
through purgation or through remedies which soak [the
stomach] and which dissolve the phlegm therefrom, and if
there are no humors which interpose between its layers,[478]
the person will have no craving at all for any of those
detrimental foods unless he is accustomed to [eating] them.

13. I do not know your[479] habit in regard to vomiting. If
vomiting is easy for you, do it in the customary manner[480]
used for cleansing the cavity of the stomach and to expel
therefrom this superfluity, as follows: take the bodies of
two or three white radishes and cut them to pieces like an
amount of nuts[481] and boil an ounce of dill[482] in a *litre* of
water; pour all this on the cut-up radishes together with
two ounces of bees' honey and an ounce or more of strong
vinegar, depending on its strength; and let it all soak
overnight. In the morning one should take an emetic
before one's usual [breakfast] and then a little unleavened
bread with various foods such as salted fish, fish brine,

melons,[483] *barkuk* plums[484] if they are in season, radish, onion, leek,[485] honey, a dish made of crushed beans,[486] and a dish made of barley with its peel. All these and their like are among the various foods which provoke vomiting and which fill [the stomach] and tarry there a little.

One should vomit everything from a raised position and nothing should remain in the stomach and it should be done at noon.[487] During the wintertime one should vomit after a bath[488] and then rest after the emesis. And one should not eat anything until one is quite hungry.[489] If one is thirsty, one should only drink apple cider. If one is very hungry one should eat small chickens or birds or turtle doves and *zarbag*.[490] One should eat good foods for several days after the vomiting until the stomach becomes strengthened.

There are some people who find it easy to vomit and they cleanse [their stomach] after vomiting from those [emetic] foods together with oxymel[491] and hot water. There are others who vomit solely from a barley dish and from drinking beer or wine; if they drink a lot of either one at one time, they vomit. All this is good. However, for someone who finds vomiting difficult and is not accustomed to it or has a reason to avoid it such as weakness of some of his organs or because of his constitution, I advise that he consume an ounce of syrup of roses and an ounce of oxymel syrup in seeds of aristolochia[492] every five days. He should wait a while and then eat his meal which should contain coarse [foods] and this cleanses the stomach of the phlegm and it will not be necessary for him to vomit.

14. If a person has a moist body and a phlegmatic constitution he should slowly swallow an ounce of oxymel in onion[493] together with an ounce of syrup of roses [cooked] in honey. And if a person with a cold stomach is even more phlegmatic, add to the aforementioned a little of the honey of

ginger syrup or the weight of half a *zuz* of [ginger] itself. If he is a young person with a warm consitution, he should take an ounce of syrup of roses and an ounce of lemon juice every five days. All this empties the stomach of phlegm and it is not necessary [for the person] to vomit if he has a contraindication as we mentioned before.

15. And I experimented upon myself and took an ounce of white sugar pulverized with half a *zuz* of anise in the cold season; during the hot season, I strengthened it with a little lemon juice. [I took this remedy] every third or fourth day as the case may be. I found that it cleansed the stomach of phlegm and emptied it well.[494] The same [effect is produced] with oxymel in quinces or lemon juice and quinces, [if used] diligently. After a few days it is beneficial to improve the digestions[495] and cleanse the stomach of phlegm. The following is its preparation: take some good quality quinces that are a little astringent and contain a little coarseness and cook them until they are reduced in half; remove their foam; take one *litre* thereof and half a *litre* of vinegar and four *litres* of sugar and honey whose foam has been removed. Place all this on the fire and add thereto one *zuz* of white pepper and two *zuzim* of ginger. Since this remedy[496] does not assuredly produce nausea, [if necessary] take more, according to the coldness of the [body] constitution and the [coldness of the] country. Sometimes one takes [only] lemon juice and, although it cannot compare with the effectiveness of vinegar in thinning the humors and opening obstructions and correcting putrefaction, nevertheless, its[497] detrimental effect is less than that [of vinegar] on the nerves and on the limbs which contain articulations.[498]

16. However, the practice of evacuation [of urine] and blood-letting or the imbibition of purgative beverages is a grave

error and is not part of the advice of the famous physicians. Indeed, it is only necessary to let blood and to purge when illnesses develop that require such action because of overfilling such as occurs if humors accumulate in the body or if [a person's] blood prevails[499] and boils because of a bad constitution or because of bad functioning; only then is it necessary [to phlebotomize or purge]. He who is accustomed to having his blood let or to drink [purgative] beverages at set intervals[500] should follow his custom but slowly increase the time between the intervals and gradually[501] reduce the amount of emptying until he reaches old age. By then the practice of bloodletting and purgation has ceased.[502]

THE TENTH CHAPTER
deals with conduct regarding sleep and awakening and washing and massaging and sexual intercourse.

1. Sleep is extremely harmful in this disease especially during an attack and especially immediately after a meal. Therefore, [patients with asthma] should sleep as little as possible.[503] Know also that sleep immediately following a meal is harmful to all people and especially to you[504] because it fills the brain with gasses.[505] If it is your custom [to sleep after meals] it is appropriate for you to occupy yourself a little after the meal, sufficient so as not to cause damage by an abrupt change in [your habit]. Gradually and slowly [increase this activity] until there is an interval of three or four hours between the meal and the sleep. Then sleep assists in the completion of the digestion[506] of the residual food which remains in the stomach. One must

be careful in [changing] any habit from one's usual bodily habit even if the latter is bad. And you should not discard it [rapidly] but gradually[507] until your nature can tolerate and adjust to it[508] as if one stole something from it. And you should not feel all this when you are healthy.[509] But when being treated for illnesses, do not consider changing your habit at all in any manner. Rather, be extremely careful [to retain your habits intact] as was elucidated to us by Galen in his book *De Usu Partium* where he describes the beneficial effects of habits as follows: he said that the various habits of all people are not of one type[510] and the [sudden] discarding of a habit can be very dangerous not only for those convalescing from illness and their like but also for those being treated for illnesses.

2. Washing is not good for you and cold water is very harmful in this illness[511] because it stops up the orifices of the body and prevents dissolution [of phlegm] which is a very important feature in this illness. Similarly, bathing is also very injurious in this illness and they[512] have already prohibited it, especially at a time close to an attack and during the attack. Beware of it even if it is your habit [to bathe]. You should try[513] to gradually increase the intervals between baths by one day [at a time] and to reduce the time spent therein, And you should be extremely careful to avoid a cold draft when you leave [the bath] and do not enter a bath when the stomach is empty.[514] And sleep for approximately one hour after the bath[515] for this is extremely beneficial for anyone who wishes to dissolve[516] thick and sticky humors, especially in this illness.

3. Galen spoke in the following words: it is appropriate for you to know that nothing compares to the efficacy of sleep after a bath with respect to digestion and in particular the spontaneous[517] dissolution of the bad humors.

4.   Says the author:[518] after I learned this [by experience] I only used to take baths at sunset and I went directly therefrom to sleep for the night.[519] And I strongly praised the feeling that I experienced from this. And it is appropriate for you[520] not to step into a basin or bathing tub filled with cold water. Rather, the water should be sufficiently hot to make the body recoil therefrom [momentarily]. And if the water is salted it is good because its effect[521] is to dry [the body] and not to moisten it. And know that excessive bathing is in general bad for all people because it putrefies the humors or prepares them for putrefaction. Physicians of our times state[522] that the rule[523] in this matter is to take at most one bath every ten days, depending on the [different] countries, the [peoples'] temperaments and their usual customs and rules. We have thus spoken about the proper habits [concerning bathing].

The pouring of lukewarm water over the head is extremely harmful to the health of all people because it increases moisture in the brain, weakens it and dissipates its strength. Similarly, the pouring of cold water over the head is extremely dangerous because it cools the brain and impedes the discharge of superfluities from the head. It is appropriate to accustom oneself to use the hottest possible water so that the skin of the head becomes red because this warms the brain, ameliorates[524] its activities and decreases the superfluities [that emanate] from it. And the skin of a person becomes firmer and stronger so that he does not become ill from the slightest reason that might affect him. Observe well all these rules in this matter.

5.   The rubbing of the entire body at the beginning of the day upon awakening and the massaging of the extremities[525] at bedtime is a good habit for all people when they are healthy. The opinions of physicians vary greatly in regard to the methods of massaging and their times of ap-

plication. It is not within the scope of this book to describe the manner of its application just as we did not mention everything that one should mention about the various types of physical exercise and massaging in [our book] *Regimen Sanitatis.*[526] The most important thing that one should do is that which I have mentioned in this treatise. The physicians of our era advocate[527] the massaging of the chest for the illness from which you suffer, and I have not found any differences of opinion nor conditions [in the application of such massages]. And I will mention the main point and the method cited by Galen of all the methods of massaging. Then I will indicate to your Highness when massaging of the chest is beneficial and when you should be careful to avoid it.

6. Galen spoke on this subject using the following words: one should be careful to avoid massaging the limbs of weak people during crises because these [massages] accentuate and aggravate their illness.[528] When they are healthy, it is proper to indulge [in massaging] more than usual, especially dry massaging. The pains which develop at times in some of the limbs as a result of this massaging prevent the occurrence [of crises] during quiet periods, especially if the massaging is performed two or three hours before the [usual occurrence] of the attack. The reason is that those limbs are strenghened thereby and the influx of [harmful] substances into them is reduced. All these things are also applicable to the elderly and to people of all ages. However, I recommend that the elderly perform far less physical exercise with weak organs than other people. The best advice for the bodies of the elderly is to rest their weak organs [as much as possible].

7. Says the author: it is evident that massaging the chest during quiet times[529] or before the occurrence of an attack is not dangerous. However, it is best to perform the

massage during a quiet time or about two hours before the [anticipated] occurrence of an attack. And it is not proper to fatigue the weak organs of the elderly at any time.

8.   It is known throughout the masses that coitus is extremely harmful to most people and excessive indulgence therein is harmful to all people. The emission of seed is not part of the preservation of health except for a few people who have bad constitutions which change because, together with the seed, fundamental humors[530] are of necessity lost[531] and the major organs become dry and cold. However, young people tolerate this transgression[532] well although some of them cannot avoid becoming ill because of it. On the other hand, coitus is harmful to the elderly because they require that which increases their warmth and moistens their organs whereas coitus extinguishes their remaining heat, as we have mentioned. It is, therefore, recommended that a person decrease his engagement in coitus according to his age. This is appropriate for the preservation of health.[533] And one should add to this the purification of the body and the soul and the acquisition of the virtues of integrity, modesty and piety.

And if coitus is harmful to all the organs in general, it is more harmful to the brain because the emptying [of superfluities] occurs from it. Hippocrates has already mentioned this [fact]. Therefore, it is appropriate that anyone with cerebral weakness for whatever reason avoid [further] weakening it [through coitus]. If one observes persons who indulge excessively in coitus, [one notes that] they suffer from memory loss and weakness of the mind[534] and of the stomach, and they develop yellowness of the face[535] and defective vision[536] and sullenness. And this matter has precedent. Just as the habits of different people vary, so do their constitutions. Physicians assert that there are some people who develop slothfulness, dejection of spirit and weakness of digestion and who, following coitus, become vibrant[537] and cheerful and with good appetite. And there are people who are just the opposite. The characteristics of people vary greatly in this matter.

Galen has already discussed one of the bad characteristics and said the following:[538] there is one body characteristic which is extremely bad and that is that there are some people who develop a lot of warm semen which arouses them and stimulates them to expel it. And when they expel it by means of coitus, their stomach weakens, their entire body weakens and becomes flaccid and dry and lean and their appearance changes and their eyes become sunken. If they abstain from coitus because of the bad effects which it produces in them their head becomes heavy and their stomach also develops heaviness and pain, and abstinence does not benefit them very much at all. And if they suffer a nocturnal pollution, the same harm occurs to them as occurs when they engage in coitus.

9. Says the author: my intention in discussing this subject is to point out the variations in the constitutions of people in this matter. And it is not the intent of this treatise to discuss the therapy of every occurrence that might happen to every individual person because that would involve the entire art of medicine. The general rule in this matter is that you should try to maintain your usual habit [of coitus] and diminish therefrom gradually and, as is proper for this illness,[539] according to one's age, as I mentioned earlier. And know that coitus is not good for any person shortly after a bath[540] nor following physical exercise nor near daybreak nor within two days of imbibing asparagus,[541] so that there should not occur a simultaneous accumulation of two discharges[542] which weaken the person. One should also not engage [in coitus] when one is hungry nor when one is replete with food, but at a time when the food has left

the stomach before hunger has begun [to be felt]. The harm
that comes from the act of coitus while one is hungry is
greater than that from the act performed when one is
satiated. Coitus practiced by a person who suffers from an
exhausting[543] illness is dangerous and may be fatal. And I
personally observed and others also observed and told me
that a person once engaged in coitus while he was sick with
an acute febrile illness; he lost his strength on that very day
and he developed a heart attack and died during that night.

10. Having completed[544] these chapters which constitute a
type of regimen of health and having finished the arrange-
ment of dietary and other regimens, it is appropriate that
we now add to these a description of the therapeutic
measures for this illness[545] and those measures to be used
during an acute attack and before and shortly after it.

THE ELEVENTH CHAPTER
describes therepeutic measures for this illness.

1. In this illness attention should be paid to insure cleanliness
of the body through regulation of the entire brain in
general with compounded medications whose action is to
expel changing and thick humors, and cleanliness of the
lungs in particular. [One must also insure] the strengthening of the brain so that it not receive nor generate nor
discharge superfluities and the strengthening of each
individual organ in general, unless one is dealing with a
vital organ.[546] In such a case, one must [diligently insure]
the expulsion of any superfluity and the restoration of [the
organ's] constitution, that is to say that it return to its
natural constitution, for every organ can eliminate bad

superfluities when it has its natural constitution and is strong. If it is affected by an illness, although we strengthen each organ to restore it to its natural constitution we must also add something with astringent properties to the remedies being used, according to its needs. A specific [enumeration of these remedies] would be lengthy and is not within the scope of this treatise.

2. And physicians have already described certain types of remedies to ameliorate [the symptoms of] this illness. All[547] physicians recommend the use of medications which produce rubefaction of the head even if they are caustic. Their intent therewith is to prevent catarrh. This [treatment], however, is not at all appropriate for you[548] because your brain is [already] warm and certainly such [new] strong warmth[549] will produce weakness, even if that warmth dries up the excessive material, expels it and prevents it from flowing. And physicians have also described powders and salves which strengthen the brain[550] in this illness. However, all have warming effects and it is not appropriate for you to use remedies which strongly warm.

It is also not appropriate to strengthen the brain with only cooling remedies because of the nature of the illness. It is thus difficult to cure it with such opposing remedies, and errors may result therefrom. In any event one should compound medications whose effects are variable.[551] However, the cleansing of the lungs requires medications which dissolve and liquify [the phlegm]. But Galen and all his successors were careful to insure[552] that these remedies not have an excessive warming effect but should have an extreme thinning effect so that they not combine with the humors in the lungs and dissolve their phlegm so that the thick substance therein not congeal and become mixed in [with the remedies] and difficult to eliminate.[553] In any event, there should be moisture mixed in with them[554] so as to aid in expectoration. The same applies to catarrhs. Sometimes the discharge which flows down from the brain is the cause of discomfort and inability to sleep and sometimes it causes the pressure if it has already reached the lungs. Sometimes the descending secretion from the brain[555] is sharp and thick[556] and requires a remedy which thins and dissolves[557] it and this increases the flow of the secretion eventhough the secretion remains. Other times the [catarrh] which descends from the head is cold and of thick consistency eventhough the brain is warm. This [situation] can occur in any organ, — that is to say sometimes it happens that the superfluity in the organ has the opposite characteristic of the principal or vital organ itself. Yet other times the matter which reaches the lungs is liquid and does not leave nor can it be expelled until its substance thickens and becomes a little sticky. I have not heard that these things have occurred to you.[558] Because of these varying conditions, in order to know them and to act appropriately, it is necessary for you to be under the observation of an expert physician at all times. That physician will establish the true situation so that he will know how to act and whether he should lean in one direction or follow two different [therapeutic] paths and prescribe a compound remedy containing both. You can readily observe that they rely on all that is written in the books [of medicine] and all that is mentioned therein about illnesses, and that illnesses vary from person to person according to their varying constitutions.

3.   The empiricists are [often] in error because they do not rely on scientific logic;[559] sometimes they are successful by pure chance and sometimes they are not successful. For this reason, I assert that he who places his life in the hands of an experienced physician who has no scientific knowledge[560]

is like a mariner who places his [trust entirely] on the blowing of the winds which do not follow scientific logic. Sometimes they blow in the direction desired by the mariner according to his plan and sometimes they cause his drowning and his death. And I warn you[561] to avoid this because there are many people who died during an experiment [at the hands] of the empiricists; and those who escaped [death] and those who succumbed did so [entirely] by chance.

4. Hippocrates said: experience [alone] is dangerous. Galen and many of his subsequent disciples also wrote that medicines should be compounded with logic and with human intellect, according to the varying characteristics of different people.[562] Among the remedies for this illness are [the following]: enemas administered at the time of an attack to drain the thick humor; and inhaled fumigations to strengthen the brain and to dry any humors that might be in it and to prevent their dripping. And I will also mention two or three medications or more of each of the types of remedies for this illness[563] which are appropriate for you and which are suitable for your constitution and upon which we know you can rely. Sometimes take one and sometimes the other for this is the recommendation of the best physicians[564] in general and for this illness in particular; that is to say to pass from one medication to another eventhough the [curative] power of all the compounded medications and their effect are similar one to the other. It is not within the scope of this treatise to describe this matter in greater detail.

The sequence of remedies which you[565] should use is to [first] strengthen the brain with that which I will mention to you when I describe the compounded medications[566] and [then] to cleanse [the body] with a purgative remedy as I will describe for you and of which there are a large number of formulas. If you find yourself very full of humors, [use these remedies] twice a year; but if you feel light, once a year is sufficient[567] during the spring season.[568] The same is true of beverages if you feel greatly filled.[569] I am confident that if you follow these rules[570] that I have mentioned you will only need a mild [purgative] medication once a year in the springtime. And when an attack [of asthma] occurs, begin drinking one of the beverages that I will describe for you. And I will begin with the least diluted. And you should dilute the food very well, and choose the beverages made only with sugar, and chicken soup, and an infusion of one of the decoctions that I will describe that assists in expectoration. And if you have fever, take some sweetened barley soup before bedtime. If you have no fever, take soup made from very old chickens. If this [remedy] is sufficient and the lungs are cleansed and the attack passes, nothing else is needed. But if the attack does not subside with this [remedy] and the lungs are not cleansed, turn to the next stronger beverage. And if the beverages are insufficient, administer one of the enemas that I will describe and begin with the mildest of them. And if it weakens you, do not drink a purgative beverage. And if this [remedy] is not sufficient, begin to drink one of the purgative drinks so as to cleanse the body in general at known times.

5.   And begin with the mildest of them which is barley soup. If it is sufficient, good; if not drink a stronger one. In addition, be careful to strengthen the brain with aromatic substances and to fumigate with fumigants that I will describe and use an infusion of those decoctions which cleanse the lungs. If the lung is relieved, its catarrh stops. However, as long as the catarrh is present and you feel it dripping, do not turn to any treatment before you have stopped it[571] with that which I will mention unless the

lungs are full [of catarrh] and respiration is impeded[572] because of it. In that case pay attention to cleanse the lungs gradually[573] with all the remedies that I have recommended. But if the illness worsens and the matter becomes aggravated, Heaven forbid, it is at least necessary to vomit repeatedly.[574] In all these situations it is necessary to be extremely careful to avoid sleep and especially sleep during the daytime. And one should not seek out sleep; on the contrary, one should avoid it [as long as possible] and then sleep a little in a sitting position. And one should be supported on all sides.[575] And beware of bad water[576] and only use it to quench [extreme] thirst. Similarly, beware of [excessive] bathing and physical exercise. However, mild gradual exercise is beneficial during the peak of the attack.

THE TWELFTH CHAPTER

deals with the compounding of various medications necessary for the various types of this illness.[577] According to the intent of this treatise, this includes beverages whose effect is to cook [the humors] and to alleviate expectoration and cleanse the lungs. And these [remedies] are those which should precede [the use of] purgatives.

1. The first [remedy] with which one should commence at the beginning of an attack is the following: two ounces each of liquorice,[578] mallow[579] and oxtongue,[580] three *zuzim* of fleabane,[581] and six hearts of green fennel.[582] Boil all these and strain over julep juice.[583]

   Another similar [remedy consists of] a handful of green fennel, ten dried figs, four *zuzim* of fleabane, boiled and stirred and strained and imbibed with sugar or honey or their like.

Another stronger [remedy consists of] four *zuzim* of fleabane,[584] three *zuzim* of the skin of fennel roots, two *zuzim* each of liquorice and mallow, one *shekel* each of mallow root and lemon[585] peel, and half an ounce of dried raisins without pits, boiled and stirred and strained with sugar or julep. If you wish to increase its expectorative effect, strain it in *sakangbin* liquor.[586]

Another still stronger [remedy] which powerfully cleanses the lungs of the thick humors[587] consists of three *zuzim* each of basilic[588] and pennyroyal,[589] two *zuzim* of dried hyssop, one *shekel* each of styrax,[590] Damascene ginger also called *rassin* and known to the Egyptian physicians[591] by the name of *ganach*, and the small centaury,[592] and six figs. Boil [all these ingredients] and strain with bees' honey. This remedy should not be taken if there is fever.

Another still stronger [remedy consists of] one *zuz* each of thyme,[593] liquorice,[594] prassion[595] and madder;[596] four *zuzim* each of balsam [resin] and its bark,[597] and spikenard;[598] two *zuzim* each of mentastrum,[599] camomile root[600] and small centaury;[601] and five *zuzim* each of dried figs and raisins without pits. Cook all [these ingredients] and stir and strain over oxymel. This [remedy] has a strong cleansing effect and prevents head catarrh[602] but one should not take it if one has fever. But in the case of fever and if the substance[603] is thin one should not deviate from using liquid remedies of simple composition and these are: pulegium,[604] liquorice, oxtongue,[605] endive seed, fennel, moist[606] or dried waterlily,[607] cucumber seeds,[608] garden rocket,[609] sabutan[610] and sempervivum,[611] according to what is available.[612] One need not be concerned with the amount [consumed] and one should mix it with liquid oxymel or with inula[613] syrup. One can also place [the aforementioned ingredients] in fresh or dried inula juice according to the judgment of the physician as to what should be done in the presence of fever. If the fever is mild there is no harm in adding thereto raisins without pits and figs. Rhazes said that if a patient with this illness[614] drinks some scolopendrium,[615] which is also called *akraban*, together with fig juice, he expels much putrefied phlegm; and it is a marvelous [remedy].

2. Says the author: that which Rhazes described and tested is supported by logic.[616] The method[617] which is well known to us in the West and which is applied according to the situation at hand and which cleanses the lungs and dries them and facilitates breathing and suppressed cough is to soak wheat bran in hot water for one night. Stir and strain it and add to the strainer sugar and almond oil. Then boil it until it develops the consistency of julep and drink it while it is lukewarm. And if one adds thereto bitter and sweet almond hearts after they are well pounded into a powder, [the resultant remedy] is extremely beneficial. One can also soak liquorice with the wheat bran. All these combinations are extremely beneficial in this illness, are widely used,[618] and one need not be afraid of them even in the presence of fever.

3. The following are some of the potions[619] which cleanse the lungs and cook that which is within them and facilitate expectoration and have a clearly beneficial effect on labored respiration and can be taken throughout the illness and at any time during the day or night:

Two equal parts of raisins without pits and fenugreek all cooked in clear water, strained and the water removed and left alone. Drink therefrom many times day after day after rewarming it. This is what Galen said and he describes it as being of great benefit. Other later physicians describe a different composition as follows: cook fenugreek and figs together and strain the water and add honey thereto and make a liquid potion therefrom. Another strong remedy recommended by Galen: take the scilla onion,[620] squeeze it and add some honey to the juice which is expressed from it and prepare a potion therefrom and take an ounce before meals and the same after the meal.

Another extremely strong remedy mentioned by Galen is the following: equal parts of mountain and river mentastrum,[621] thyme,[622] sassan roots which is lily,[623] white pepper, and roasted anise.[624] Grind all these and sift them in a coarse sifter and knead in cooked honey. Take an amount equal to the size of one nut.

Another stronger potion recommended by later physicians is the following: three ounces each of round aristolochia and fenugreek flour, two ounces of myrrh,[625] and one ounce of madder tincture.[626] Grind all these and take an amount equal to the size of a nut.

Another beneficial but milder potion recommended by later physicians and which is especially suitable for you[627] is the following: take some of the large pine fruits[628] which have a large amount of resin and cook them with fresh marrubium[629] of a quantity half of that of the fruit. Strain and mix the resultant liquid with some pure honey and cook it until it develops the consistency of the honey. Take some of this potion because it cleanses all that is within the chest with a marvelous cleansing.

That which you are accustomed to taking during various circumstances [of your health] consists of an ounce of pulverized and sifted liquorice[630] juice and two ounces each of peeled bitter almonds[631] and *panid.*[632] The almonds are pounded until they are pulverized[633] and the entire mixture is dissolved in fennel water and boiled on a low fire until it becomes a potion.[634] I prefer to add lemon juice which is like *hiliyon*[635] as a substitute for the *panid* and I also add thereto a decoction of basil[636] and almond oil and this becomes an electuary which is beneficial for all our expectations.[637]

4. And it is appropriate to warn you that you should be careful to always have available to you the opium potion described by Galen because it prevents catarrh, favors sleep, thickens thin material and assists in expectoration. The formula is as follows: ten *zuzim* of liquorice, poppy, completely ripe[638] white fresh nuts and ten heads of vegetable troches, all crushed until they resemble seeds and soaked in hot water overnight. In the morning, boil [the mixture] and strain it with a *litre* of grape juice or a *litre* of sugar and a *litre* of bees' honey. Make it into a beverage and take it by the spoonful[639] when necessary. The potion made from bees' honey cleanses the lungs better[640] but it should not be taken in case of warm, thick catarrh; the potion made with grape juice is better than the former in preventing catarrh; and the one made with sugar is intermediate between them. And when the catarrh becomes lighter or if the flow of phlegm ceases completely except for that which remains in the lungs, do not drink any one of these potions unless the material in the chest is thin and cannot be expelled because of its thinness and requires something to thicken it. Then the procedure for you should be to take tragacanth[641] and gum arabic,[642] pulverize them and dissolve them in the above potion over a soft fire and take it by the spoonful a little at a time.[643] And take equal parts of poppy seeds, alcohol, sugar and starch; grind everything in the juice of plantago psyllium and take some by the spoonful a little at a time[644] or knead [the poppy seeds] in the juice of quince seeds.[645] And to all this you can mix in violet syrup.

5.   I once personally compounded a remedy for a woman whose condition I examined thoroughly. My intent therewith was to cleanse the lungs, strengthen the brain and stop the catarrhs. She did not have an excessively warm constitution. When this illness affected her, she was menstruating,[646] her brain was not hot nor was it abnormally cold, and her body was lean. And this remedy benefitted her greatly during attacks.[647] And although she ceased taking it when she was well,[648] the attacks became less frequent until she reached the point where she only had one attack per year and later only one in two years. And even then the attack was attenuated.[649] In the preparation of this remedy, I conformed to the opinion of Galen who said that remedies which produce a great beneficial effect are those prepared from different medications which vary not only in their nature but also in their strengths. The following is how I prepared it:

I took an indeterminate quantity[650] of basil[651] and soaked it in hot water. Then I cooked it and strained it and added to the strainer an indeterminate amount of pulegio.[652] I boiled and strained it a second time and put it aside. I did the same with liquorice: I crushed it, soaked it and cooked it alone once. Then I strained it and replaced it on the fire until it developed the consistency of honey and I set it aside. Next I took two glasses of pulegio decoction and one glass of liquorice decoction because of its thicker consistency and one glass of green fennel juice and two glasses of grape juice with a consistency of honey. And I mixed all these and I placed this mixture on a low fire and cooked it. And I removed the foam that formed from the fennel juice and discarded it.[653] This is an excellent electuary with a consistency of honey and a pleasant taste. This electuary is without doubt very efficacious for this illness.

Afterwards I assembled the following medications: three ounces of nettles,[654] once ounce each of soaked, washed pine kernels and roasted linseed,[655], half an ounce each of *sozan* root,[656] long and round aristolochia, inula,[657] spikenard,[658] radish seed,[659] tincture of rubia, and horehound,[660] ten *zuzim* each of hartstongue[661] and cumin,[662] two *zuzim* of curcuma, and three *zuzim* of myrrh. The total number of ingredients[663] is thirteen[664] and the total weight is approximately seventeen ounces. And I crushed and sifted all that could be sifted; however, I pulverized and ground the seeds and kernels which could not be sifted until they became soft and resembled marrow. And I kneaded the entire mixture over a low fire with four *litres* of the aforementioned electuary which has the consistency of honey. I have not seen this preparation described by any of the ancient or contemporary physicians. It is indeed based on logic.[665] I have already related to you the success that I obtained therewith.[666] I, therefore, advise you[667] to always have it available and to use it regularly[668] during periods of health and during attacks [of asthma] except if you have a high fever, Heaven forbid.

6. We have already mentioned that the soup of old chickens assists in the cooking and expectoration [of phlegm]. However, to strengthen the brain in this illness, Ibn Zuhr asserts that he found powders better than pomade.[669] As I already informed you excessive heat is not appropriate for this illness nor is severe cold. In my opinion, the following [pomade] is proper: three *zuzim* of muscat blossom, two *zuzim* each of pine[670] and sandalwood[671] from Katzir, a *shekel* of myrrh, and a quarter *zuz* of old camphor; grind all these well and sift and knead with rosewater and make troches therefrom. Take one of the troches, pulverize it and apply the powder to a site devoid of hair. On hot days,

dissolve it in rosewater and during the cold season rub the middle of the head with quince oil and place the powder thereon. The preparation of the quince oil is as follows: take an ounce of fragrant rose oil and squeeze a quince into it; add half a *zuz* of mastic and a quarter *zuz* of santalum.[672] Place all this on hot cinders until the liquid[673] evaporates and the oil remains. Set it aside [until needed as mentioned]. Know also that amber[674] strengthens both a cold and a warm brain.

We have also heard from the elders[675] — who knew this by experience — that chicory[676] is efficacious both for a cold and a warm liver. Therefore, I advise you to regularly use this fragrance and to make fumigations only with it because it fortifies the brain and prevents it from receiving and from producing superfluities.

Another remedy is as follows: take four *zuzim* of myrobalan oil without any other drugs and without color and dissolve in it a *shekel* of fresh amber, half a *shekel* of pulverized and sifted sandalwood from Katzir, and a quarter *zuz* of old camphor. Make all this into an unguent and rub it on the middle of the head and on the forehead[677] about a half hour after leaving the bath.[678] You should regularly[679] apply this ointment on cold days but decrease its use on hot days but do not interrupt using it even during attacks.

Contemporary physicians[680] describe other fumigants which strengthen the brain and dry out its superfluous humors and prevent them from spreading [to other organs]. Among them is aloe which should be cast onto the fire so that the resultant vapor enters the nostrils. This is a hightly effective and tested remedy.[681] Another remedy is to take equal parts of costus, liquidamber,[682] fresh anise,[683] red orpiment,[684] gum resin,[685] incense,[686] galbanum[687] and mastic. Mix everything and place it on the fire until the vapors ascend and let them enter the mouth and the nostrils to fill the head and the chest. This remedy is completely efficacious. Another remedy consists of orpiment with long aristolochia, crushed and kneaded with ox fat and used as a fumigation [over a fire].

7.   Among enemas, the mildest consists of half a *litre* of beet juice[688] and four ounces of sesame oil; boil these, add a *zuz* of natron[689] and use as an enema. A stronger one consists of oil in which wine was boiled; add a *zuz* of natron and use as an enema. A stronger one consists of oil in which wine was boiled; add a little natron or borax and use as an enema. Stronger yet is [an enema made from] a handful each of mentha and anise, half a *litre* of beet juice and a *litre* of fine oil; boil everything and add a little natron and use as an enema. An even stronger enema consists of a fistful each of anise, mentha and centaury;[690] boil all these in water and add thereto two ounces of fine oil and honey and cassia fistula; administer it when it is tepid. And if the patient has marked flatulence,[691] it is beneficial to add half an ounce of cumin,[692] and mix duck fat or chicken fat into the oil in all the aforementioned enemas.

An even stronger enema is to add to the above enema one half to two *zuzim* of colocynth; boil it as described above and use as an enema. And if one also adds thereto camomile,[693] millet[694] and *gundabadstur,*[695] one obtains a perceptibly stronger enema. These hot[696] enemas should not be used on hot days[697] nor if one has fever. No person has need of them unless he has very thick humors or severe constipation.

8.   Galen has already cautioned against[698] the use of hot enemas in old people at any time. Know that it is just as inappropriate to administer very hot enemas as it is to administer strong purgatives unless it is done on the advice

of an expert physician who is physically present and not giving advice from afar.

However, among the purgatives commonly used are the following purgative preparations which expel white humors[669] and cleanse the head: a *shekel* of hiera picra,[700] half a *zuz* each of agaric[701] and *turbid,*[702] and a quarter *zuz* of ginger; take this [mixture] by the spoonful in julep. Another stronger purgative to cleanse the lungs consists of half a *shekel* of agaric, half a *zuz* of aristolochia, and a quarter *zuz* of anise. Another yet stronger purgative to cleanse the lungs consists of half a *shekel* of opoponax, a *zuz* of hiera picra, and a quater *zuz* of colocynth, prepared with an equal quantity of pistachio kernel, and tragacant resin;[703] drink this potion.[704]

Another stronger purgative which is an efficacious combination which you[705] should use at intervals and during a strong attack[706] is the following: half a *zuz* each of agaric and *turbid*, a *zuz* of hiera picra, a quarter *zuz* each of myrrh, and the root of *susan*[707] and *prassion,*[708] a quarter *zuz* of sarcocolla, an eighth *shekel* each of anise, colocynth, *dragakant,*[709] and blue bdellium; knead [all these ingredients] in grape juice.

Another yet stronger purgative consists of one *shekel* each of *turbid*, agaric, cucumber juice[710] and absinth,[711] a *zuz* of hiera picra, a quarter *zuz* each of colocynth and astragalus gummifier;[712] knead [all these ingredients] in fennel water and make pills therefrom with [hazel] nut oil. Another yet stronger purgative which cleanses the lungs very well consists of one-eighth *shekel* each of colocynth and astragalus, half a *shekel* each of anise, epithyme,[713] serapinum[714] and aristolochia, kneaded in honey water. Another still stronger [laxative remedy consists of] one *zuz* each of urtica[715] and polypodium[716] seeds and cucumber[717] juice which is *kogelmari*. Another purgative consists of a quarter *zuz* of colocynth, a quarter *zuz* each of astragalus gummifier and bdellium judaicum, three pistachio nuts,[718] kneaded in celery water[719] and pills made therefrom with nut oil; this remedy expels the many bad, thick and sticky humors.

Know that all these strong purgatives are beneficial in this illness.[720] However, if there is need to only treat the intestines, purgation with mild laxatives such as cassia fistula and rhubarb is not harmful. But cassia fistula and rhubarb have no efficacy in cleansing the head nor in cleansing the lungs.

9. And I will now describe for you the formulas of all the therapeutic purgative preparations which the best physicians in the West tested and which we ourselves observed and often tested ourselves and found to be very effective purgatives. Agaricon should be split over a sieve until it is sifted. *Turbid* should be peeled at the top,[721] crushed and sifted. So too, it is good to sift hiera picra. Colocynth, however, should be cut as finely as possible with scissors and only the white part thereof should be taken which is freed from the large fruit in which it is found. And one should be very careful [to avoid] putrefied *turbid*. Astragalus should be soaked and removed from the [sifting] cloth.

Any medication containing colocynth or colocynth leaves should be prepared as follows: crush the stalk and add the colocynth or its cut up leaves and crush pistachio kernels after shelling them with a knife and add these thereto. Then remove the astragalus from the cloth and add thereto the colocynth and its accessory[722] and pound everything until it becomes a single flat cake. Then add to it[723] the hiera picra and the other sifted ingredients. However, the scammony[724] and the mastic should not be finely ground. The same applies to other purgative medications except those which are mentioned which should remain the size of barley, that is to say one should not grind them finely nor sift them, especially myrobalan[725] which should not be sifted but remain the size of barley. Everything should be kneaded in one of the liquids and pills made therefrom with almond oil. If your intent is to cleanse the rest of the body the pills should be small and moist and taken early in the morning. And if you have pain or spasm in the stomach, boil three *zuzim* weight of oxtongue,[726] a *shekel* of stoechus,[727] and half a *zuz* of *ethrog*[728] and colocynth. Imbibe it in sips or strain it over sugar and drink it because it calms the pain and allows the medication to act.[729]

10.   All these formulas[730] I received from the Western sages.[731] Only little thereof is mentioned in medical books and [even] these are not known to most people. [I enumerated them here] because my intent was to provide great benefit to all people as much as possible. However [to describe] the action of each purgative medication and its cessation or the effect of discontinuing it or its augmentation or the treatment of various situations which might arise because of it is an important subject[732] in medical science but is beyond the scope of this treatise. The therapeutic effects vary according to the different medications used and the different ages and constitutions [of the patients] and the climate[733] and the seasons of the year.

As for emetics, if one has need of them, one should begin with the consumption of radish and then take two *zuzim* of borax with about half a *litre* of honey water. Another stronger emetic is the following: take some pieces of white veratrum[734] and of its stalks and mix them with radish and [also] drink water and honey[735] and you will vomit. Another yet stronger emetic consists of half a *zuz* each of mustard,[736] salt and Armenian borax,[737] and two *danik*[738] of natron, all dissolved in three ounces of water and an ounce of honey. Drink this potion and you will vomit.

11. It is clear that the intent of this treatise is not to enumerate all the therapeutic methods for this illness but to describe those that are easily applied. I have, therefore, written for your Highness that which I think [useful for you] which more than answers your question.

THE THIRTEENTH CHAPTER

mentions certain passages, few in number but of great benefit to all people in general in relation to the preservation of health[739] and the use of medicines. These passages are like commandments.[740]

1. It is appropriate to first pay attention to the improvement of the air, then to the amelioration of the water [one drinks], and to the improvement of one's diet.[741] There are what the physicians call spirits which are the light winds[742] which are found in living organisms. They originate and derive most of their substance from the air inhaled from the outside. The pneuma[743] of the blood which is found in the liver is called the natural spirit and the pneuma that is found in the heart and great vessels[744] is called the vital spirit, and the pneuma that is found in the ventricles of the brain and which is sent from there to the various nerves is called the animal spirit.[745] All these pneumas originate and derive most of their substance from the air inhaled from the outside. And if that air is mouldy, malodorous or turbid,[746] all these spirits become modified and their action is the opposite of what it should be.

2.   Galen said: pay attention to the quality[747] of the air which enters the body so that the quality and composition[748] and purity should be without any waste mixed in.[749]

3.   Says the author: the lighter and thinner the body spirit,[750] the more it changes with changes in the air. Thus the natural spirit is denser than the vital spirit and the vital spirit is denser than the animal spirit. The slightest change in the air causes a change in the character of one's soul[751] which one can feel. Because of this, with a decrease in the quality of the air, many people feel a diminution of their intellectual functions,[752] that is to say they develop stupor, decreased ability to comprehend and memory loss even-though their natural and vital activities undergo no change.

4.   The relationship between the air of cities and its streets and the air of open fields and deserts is comparable to the relationship between thick, turbid water and clear, light water. This means that cities, because of their buildings, the narrowness of their street, the refuse and wastes of their inhabitants, their corpses and animal carcasses, and the putrefaction of their foods, provoke stagnation of the air which becomes turbid and thick and penetrates the buildings and is carried stealthily by the winds, and a person becomes ill without feeling it. And if we cannot find a way to escape from this after having grown up in cities and become accustomed thereto, one should at least choose a city with wide horizons, preferably in a north easterly direction and, if possible, on a sloping wooded mountainside where there is little water.[753] And if it is not possible for you to do so, that is to move from one town to another town, at least try to live at the outskirts of the city[754] on the eastern[755] side or the northern side. And your living quarters should be on an upper floor with large

[rooms] so that the northern wind can traverse them and the sun can shine in[756] because the sun melts putrefactions in the air and renders them fine and clear. One should pay attention to locate toilets as far removed as possible from one's living quarters. And one should strive to improve the air and to dry it with aromatic, scented substances and fumigations and perfumes as appropriate according to the changes in the air. This is the essential goal with which to begin the regimen for preserving the health of one's body and soul.

5. Even if you are careful and prudent to the utmost of your ability, minor events nevertheless constantly develop in the human body. For example, sometimes mild diarrhea occurs[757] whereas othertimes constipation develops.[758] One day a person finds a change in his digestion or suffers from a mild headache or has mild pain in another part of his body. In such a case, one should be very prudent and careful not to immediately treat this condition and not to quickly take medicines to eliminate it. The most eminent[759] of physicians have already warned us against such [precipitous intervention] because in such cases nature alone is sufficient [to correct the malady] and there is no need to resort to medicine. A good regimen of health is adequate because if you begin to treat a mild malady you will not be able to avoid two things: either your [therapeutic] action is in error and contrary to the needs of nature thus impeding the cure[760] and aggravating the malady, or your [therapeutic] action is correct and nature returns to its normal functioning but you thereby teach your nature laziness and accustom it not to do the proper thing without external help and assistance. An analogy to this situation, they say, is when a person teaches his animal not to walk unless told to do so[761] and the animal remains still until it is prodded.[762] The situation is also similar to a

person who develops diarrhea which is unusual for him, but without any change in his customary regimen and which lasts for two or three days without producing pain or attenuation of his strength. If one immediately uses things with astringent action and stops the diarrhea and returns nature to its normal condition with the use of medications, one may thereby cause the impedence of the excretory movements of nature[763] which excrete that which should be excreted and thus nature becomes weakened.[764] If it is withheld and impedes nature, its proper function is confused and suspended, that which should be excreted is retained and troubles develop. Sometimes the cause of the diarrhea[764a] is weakness of the retentive force but, if left alone, the organ rapidly recovers and returns to its normal functioning. However, if this force is strengthened with medications at a time when it is fatigued,[765] it becomes accustomed thereto and [always] requires external stimulation. Thus is apparent the justification of leaving the matter alone and not interfering.[766] The same should be done in any situation where there is no danger to life.

6.   Abu-Nasser Alfarabi[767] has already mentioned that the efforts applied in the practice of medicine, in seamanship and in agriculture, are not necessarily related to the results obtained. Thus, the physician may do everything that is appropriate, with great perfection, without there being any error on his part or on the part of the patient, yet the patient does not recover nor become healed which is the [ultimate] goal. The reason [for this failure] is clear in that the cure[768] is dependent not only on medicine but on medicine and nature combined. Sometimes nature does not react for a variety of reasons some of which we have mentioned in this treatise. The same may occur to the cultivator of the land who does everything appropriately but his plantings[769] are not successful. So, too, the seaman

navigates his ship in the best possible manner and builds it [masterfully] and sets out on the ocean at the most propitious time, yet the ship is dashed to pieces.[770] The reason for all these [failures] is the fact that the goal is dependent upon two factors one of which is perfectly performed but the other's action is deficient.

7. And if you pay close attention to this aforementioned section, you will notice that sometimes the illness is mild and nature is stronger than it and begins to remove it and tries to do all that which should be done.[771] But the physician or the patient may err in what they do thereby nullifying the actions of nature. This happens often in all cities and during all times.

8. In one of his aphorisms, Rhazes[772] expresses himself as follows: if the illness is stronger than the strength [of the patient], medicine is not beneficial. If the strength [of the patient] can overpower the illness, there is no need whatsoever for a physician. But if they are equal, the physician is needed to reinforce the strength [of the patient] and assist him in overcoming the illness.[773]

9. Says the author: from the words of this man who is perfect in his art it is known that he who can manage without a physician is greater than one who needs one when one considers all illnesses. This is so if he[774] is distinguished and knows how to assist nature in someone where it is confused and deflected from its normal habits.[775]

10. How great is the sin of famous physicians who commit grave errors on people without the patient succumbing and in fact surviving. I have often[776] observed a strong purgative administered to someone who does not even need a mild purgative; and the person bled copiously from

below[777] until he developed diarrhea and tenesmus, yet recovered.

In another case, I observed bloodletting from a patient with a gastric malady[778] where the physician did not know about the gastric malady. The patient developed faintness[779] and his strength left him and his illness became protracted and more intense. Yet later he recovered and it was not known why. And people think that errors of physicians cause little harm. And they say: if such grave errors committed [by physicians] do not result in the death of patients, how can they die if the physician commits a small error in the [prescription of the] correct amount of a food or a beverage? The matter is not so, however, because the explanation for these types of occurrences[780] lies in unknown suppositions.[781] Thus one observes people whose arms are amputated from the elbow or whose legs [are cut off] from the knee or whose eyes have been enucleated or who have sustained deep abdominal wounds by a sword and who do not die but, in fact, live as willed by the Creator. [On the other hand], one finds a person who is pricked by a small needle or sharp [thorn] which affects his nerves and he dies.[782] By analogy, the same applies to a physician's error, for he may commit a grave error and the patient survives. And people pay no attention[783] to a small error[784] which may cause the patient pain and suffering and even be the cause of the patient's death in spite of the smallness of the error. Anyone with good introspection should deliberate on this matter.

11. It is known that a person thinks that since customary eating and customary drinking of water and washing in cold water to one who is accustomed thereto or bathing [in hot water is not harmful], there is no great danger to a patient if he does these things in the opposite manner of what he should. But the matter is [really] not so because

Galen has already elucidated for us that in some febrile patients who drink cold water excessively, their humors become unripe, their fever increases and they die. And there are other patients for whom the imbibition of cold water is a therapeutic remedy which loosens their bowels,[785] decreases their fever[786] and they recover; if water is withheld from them, they would perish and die. The same applies to febrile patients: some who are taken [to bathe] in cold water recover and are cured whereas others die. Similarly, some febrile patients who take hot baths[787] to cleanse the body are completely cured whereas others suffer from worsening of the putrefaction[788] and their fever increases and they may die.

The same applies to food; withholding it from a patient can be the cause of his recovery or the cause of his death. The reasons for all these matters and the conditions which are dependent upon them as well as the individual factors have already been described and elucidated by specific examples. All these [difficult things] can be very easily understood by an intelligent person from books. To a person ignorant in the basic principles of these arts, nothing seems difficult and they do not see that every illness requires [careful] meditation.

12.   In one of his aphorisms, Rhazes states that in books medicine is described as an art. Some physicians aggrandize it but conscientious physicians know how difficult it is.

13.   Says the author: concerning the matter which Rhazes cites in this aphorism, Galen has already written[789] books thereon stating: how can some of our medical colleagues consider this art to be so simple and make light of it whereas Hippocrates considered it to be profound and far reaching? However, do not, dear reader, think that this

[observation] applies only to medicine, for if you delve into the natural sciences, mathematics[790] and jurisprudence,[791] you will find the same. For the more proficient and erudite a person is in a given discipline and the more he delves into it, the more doubts he has; and [many] questions are difficult for him and he delves more into the subject[792] but he cannot provide answers. On the other hand, a person lacking in knowledge finds every difficulty[793] easy [to explain] and remote things are, in his perception, readily elucidated.[794] And his vanity is so great that he promptly gives an answer to even that which he does not understand.

And I will now return to the idea which I expressed earlier when I spoke of the facility of the art of medicine[795] for people with good intelligence and the difficulty of its practical application. Galen has already spoken of these matters and the following are his words.

14.   Galen said: we used to say that it is good to massage the elderly with oil. It seems very easy but the proper implementation of this [advice] is among the most difficult things to do.

15.   Says the author: pay attention, sincere people; if Galen considered mere massaging with oil to be one of the most difficult things to put into actual practice[796] and so too the imbibition of water or the absention therefrom as we have explained earlier, how much more so is this true in regard to bloodletting and purgation with the kernel of colocynth or cucumber juice[797] or varieties of hellebore[798] and the use of enemas of castor oil or opoponax and cauterization and the [making of] an incision.[799] All these [things] are not easy for the physician but truly difficult.

16.   In one of his famous books, Ibn Zuhr said as follows: I found this advice for you who delve into this treatise

sufficiently important to expand on it and to cite the words and commentary of Galen thereon in his own words so that you can observe and understand his statements with all your heart, word by word, with [your full] attention. After that I will describe what follows therefrom.

17. Hippocrates said: it is appropriate that you pay attention to two things; one is to benefit the patient and the other is not to harm him.

18. Galen said: At one time I thought this to be a small matter not important enough for Hippocrates to mention. I used to think that no person would doubt that most of the thoughts and concerns of the physician are to help patients and if he is unable to do so he at least does [the patient] no harm. This was my opinion before I began the study of medicine and before I began practicing it or when I was with one other [person] when I practiced it. But when I was among them[800] I observed many prominent physicians[801] practice bloodletting or prescribe bathing or the imbibition of medicine or permit the patient to drink wine and cold water. The thought entered my mind that Hippocrates also witnessed such things.[802] There is no doubt that this occurred to many of his contemporaries. After that I was extremely careful and took extra care whenever I prescribed a powerful remedy for the patient.[803] I would first deliberate with myself what effect this remedy would have, and I would not stop worrying what damage it might produce if my reasoning was incorrect. I would not act at all unless it was clear to me that if my prescription[804] would not benefit the patient, it would at least not seriously harm him.

19. Says the author: You, the reader, reflect how renowned and famous physicians during the time of Galen erred in

giving patients cold water to drink or prescribing baths thereby producing serious harm. Such also happened to Hippocrates.[805] Therefore, he was careful in this matter and warned [others] to beware therefrom. For [even] Galen, as perfect as he was in this science,[806] testified about himself that whenvever he had to prescribe any type of remedy he would not rely on his own impression or opinion but would act after careful thought and deliberation. Indeed, he would say to himself, for example: this person should have such and such a humor purged from him with such and such a drug based on this evidence. Then he would deliberate and assess whether the purgation would be beneficial [to the patient] if the condition was as it appeared to him, and not produce great harm if it was the opposite of what he thought; then he would have him drink it. But if he concluded[807] that if the matter was the opposite of what he thought, [the purgative] would cause great harm, he would not act according to his opinion and according to his logical deductions.[808] The same applies to bloodletting and similar procedures as previously mentioned.

And if Galen, in spite of his great intellect and long experience in the practice of medicine and his devotion to this art and his great diligence and thoroughness therein, would reverse his decision if he had any doubt in his [medical] practice, how [much more so] should this matter be thus[809] in those places where physicians have very little experience in medical practice; and much [experience] is needed because of the many facts one must remember and the details[810] [of medical knowledge], for a person's lifetime is too short to master them all or even [the details of] one part thereof as I explained in my *Commentary on the Aphorisms of Hippocrates*.[811] And if I spoke here at length,[812] it was to give you[813] good advice to beware of [certain] physicians and not to place your life[814] in the hands of any one of them just because he is available. Rather, rely on an excellent[815] regimen of health whose details we have already cited. The main conclusion to be drawn therefrom is that their errors [in diagnosis and therapy] are greater[816] then their correct [prescriptions].

20. In one of his famous books,[817] Aristotle expresses himself in the following manner: he says that the first thing [for a physician to do] is to examine nature such as health and illness.[818] Most physicians err in [their assessment of] this force so that the cause of the death of the person is the remedy [prescribed by the physician].

21. Says the author: in another version I saw that at this point he said that "most people die of medicine". And I say that it is appropriate to listen to Aristotle in this assessment. As you know, in his era, these [medical] sciences were [practiced] to perfection and practitioners of this art did not occupy themselves with anything else.

I have here briefly extracted for you some of the wonderful albeit little-known statements from [ancient] books to thereby call your attention to that which is generally straightforward and beneficial in [the art of] medicine.

22. I know that you[819] could say: "The conclusion to be drawn from your words is to abandon medicine because all one's efforts and toil[820] in this profession all seem to be for naught." I will dispel the doubt for you. And if it has already been stated by the ancients, I will nevertheless repeat it. Know that medicine is an absolutely essential science for man at all times and in all places, not only during times of illness but even during times of health[821] to the point where I firmly believe[822] that one should never be separated from medicine.[823] Certainly, if the physician is

perfect and has achieved the highest [level of medical knowledge and practice], a person can place his spirit and his body in his hands and be guided by the regimen he prescribes. Such physicians can be found in every place and during every era. However, a person should not rely on a physician who is not perfect and who is among the majority of practicing physicians[824] as does a person who nourishes himself with bad food if he does not find good food. For a person cannot live without food but he can survive without giving over his body and his soul to someone who has not reached wisdom [in medicine]. Rather, one should leave this matter to nature and rely on the best possible regimen according to one's best intuition.

And we have already explained that the diligent physician who is perfect in his profession and remembers well the fundamental principles [of medicine] reflects carefully and knows which fundamental principles require reflection in regard to which therapies should be used to alleviate the patient's [illness]. And he leaves [the cure] to the activity of nature so that nature not become lazy as we mentioned earlier. And he knowns which illnesses should be treated and suppressed before they prevail and become so serious that they cannot be cured. And he recognizes cases[825] of fear and fright and tries to alleviate them as Galen mentions about himself. And he knows that in cases of doubt, one should not intervene with any act at all, and he meditates about [the possibility of] abandoning medicines and relies first on the activity of nature. Even when he knows what to do, he follows the activity of nature and goes in its footsteps as Hippocrates and Galen taught us. Such [a physician] should be listened to and his prescriptions followed in all these matters. Even if he errs in one of these matters, it is only a very rare and unusual occurrence. For if a dangerously ill person[826] comes under his care, he does not overlook things which may be greatly harmful and so informs the patient.

On the other hand, [physicians] lacking [in medical knowledge and experience] do not stop treating patients even if they do not understand all these situations. Sometimes they succeed [in curing the patient] and sometimes they err. Their errors are many and their successes few and incidental. If no other physicians are available one should leave the matter to nature; sometimes it succeeds and sometimes it fails but its successes are numerous and reliable whereas its failures are few and incidental. Therefore, every intelligent person should decide in his own mind to remain with nature rather than to rely on the regimen prescribed by one lacking in [medical] knowledge. But people do not do so but unfortunately seek healing from any available [physician] for any illness that develops. And most physicians do not understand the consequences of their actions.[827] This is what Aristotle said: most people die of medicines and remedies. For this reason, I warned [you] and offered [you] advice to rely on nature because the latter is totally adequate, if left alone and not confused, for most [ailments] that might arise.

23. Hippocrates spoke in the following words: nature cures illnesses. And he also said that nature finds the proper path by itself and not by tradition [from human hands]. And he further said that nature does what should be done because it is noble and learned with a good ethic because we learn ethics from it.

24. Says the author: these statements appear often[828] in most of his books. He teaches people to learn from the acts of nature which are undoubtedly well known to experienced[829] people.

25. In one of his well known treatises, Galen spoke in the following words: the Greeks used to say that when in doubt about an illness, leave it to nature which can completely drive the illness away. In support of their view, they argue that nature is the overseer and commander of a living person when he is healthy and nourishes him when he is ill and knows the constitution of his organs and sends each organ the nourishment[830] that it needs after first preparing sites for the superfluities of the food and for the humors to be distributed within the body.[831]

26. Says the author:[832] if you reflect carefully on these words, you will find that they confirm what I mentioned earlier; namely, if one searches but cannot find a perfect[833] physician and one is also in doubt about the illness, it is proper to rely [solely] on nature as I mentioned before.

27. Having heard these words, do not conclude[834] that I am the one in whose hands you[835] should entrust the conduct of your body and soul. In fact, I call on Heaven to be my witness that I myself know that I am among those who are not perfect in this art [of medicine] and also recoil from it because of the difficulty, in my opinion,[836] of achieving its goals.[837] There is no doubt that I know myself better than anyone else and I can differentiate my knowledge and the knowledge of others from that of those who have less learning than I. And I again[838] call on Heaven to be my witness that I do not make this statement out of modesty nor in the manner of pious people who claim[839] they lack knowledge even if they are in fact perfect [in knowledge] and who minimize their deeds even if they are diligent and active. Rather, I state the truth[840] as it is. And I wrote[841] this chapter out of fear that when you[842] delve into it you might think that I did so for my own aggrandizement[843] and thus take lightly my good advice and think that lust

[for personal gain] is mixed therein. And you may minimize relying on me and not follow my advice. That is why I wrote this chapter and I will now return to complete my main theme.[844]

28. It is known among all those who delve into the art of medicine and it is known to most people that it is an art which requires both practice[845] and theory. The things which are known through practice are far more numerous than those known through theory. Because people sense this, they are very heavily guided[846] by experimentation so that the masses of people in western countries[847] say: "ask the experimenter and do not ask the physician". They harm [the reputation of medicine] and make people rely on old women's tales. Thus, any presumptious or arrogant person[848] used[849] this gate to enter [medical practice] by claiming: "I have proven remedies".[850] Many of these [peddlers of] remedies prompted people to accept them as "physicians" because they[851] thought that they[852] were experienced[853] or were advanced in years. Many people said: so and so is not among the learned [physicians] but has experience and learning and is accustomed to proficiency in practice. These are all errors which lead to all [the dangers] of which we warn.

29. The first error is that people believe that experience cited in relation to medicine refers to the experience of the [individual] physician in his own era. But the matter is not so. Rather, experience refers to that of many generations [even] before Galen and Hippocrates, and the remedies[854] which they wrote in medical books. Some medications and some compounded remedies were tested for hundreds of years and [then] written in books. But a single person practicing this art [of medicine] cannot possibly have experience to refute[855] the conditions of the experience [of centuries].[856] Even a righteous physician does not jump to

test [a new remedy] because Hippocrates said "experience may be dangerous".[857] But in our time, aggrandized people boast of experience and lead people astray[858] with an unproven remedy[859] in order to conceal therewith their own ignorance.[860]

30. Another error is [to think] that a person can become proficient in the practice of medicine without the basic knowledge.[861] On the other hand, it is possible that a person[862] is knowledgeable about the practice of medicine, expert in its various branches and major principles but does not regularly practice medicine.[863] This is possible and true if he studied from the books but did not serve the elders of this art[864] and did not engage in its practice. But for a person to be an expert because he observed and witnessed[865] its practice but has no knowledge [of medicine] is false. For the art of medicine is not like the craft of carpentry or weaving which can be learned by habit and acquired by repetitive work. For this art [of medicine] requires [theoretical] reflection and practical care. Every person who becomes ill necessarily requires fresh reflection and one should not say that this illness is like that illness. The custom has been adopted and I observed elderly [physicians] following it, — that the physician should not treat the illness but should treat the patient suffering therefrom.[866] But it is not the intent of this chapter to discuss these differences and their application.[867] The intent is for you[868] not to be endangered by becoming enticed[869] with these perceptions. You should only rely on intelligent and knowledgeable physicians[870] because [knowledge] is the root and the application thereof is the branch. There cannot be a branch without a root. However, one finds roots that have not yet grown branches as we have explained. And I have also mentioned to you in this treatise that he who places himself in the

hands of an experienced practitioner who has no [medical] knowledge but does what he pleases[871] is like a mariner who survives or drowns by pure chance.

Galen enlarged on this theme and spoke at length thereof and filled his books therewith. Among his words regarding experimentation and those who experiment is the following statement: logic[872] provides the proof for the things that you search for, but one who experiments without logic is like a blind man who cannot find his way.[873]

31. Says the author: observe how the experimenter [without knowledge] resembles a blind person; so, too, a patient who places himself in his hands resembles a mariner. You should know this and beware not to fall into his hands.

32. That which I mentioned before that a physician may occasionally err[874] by prescribing water or the abstention therefrom or bathing in a bathhouse thereby causing great harm is indeed true as I described in the name of Galen. However, such is an unusual and rare occurrence. Nevertheless, I emphasized it so that you should not rely on physicians who are not perfect in [their knowledge of] strong remedies. Among all the strong remedies, there are none stronger than bloodletting and the imbibition of purgatives; next are vomiting and drastic enemas. And one should not rely on anyone who happens to be available. Yet behold the manner of people, both healthy and ill, who rely on barbers for bloodletting and on youngsters[875] for the imbibition of purgatives.

Galen has already explained and clarified that it is a medical rule that some patients should not have blood let from them unless there are signs[876] which point to an overfilling.[877] The same rule applies in regard to purgation of the intestines and emesis. The reason for this is, as he mentioned, related to the type of illness and its severity and to the inherent[878] strength [of the patient]. He also explained to us that sometimes there are clear signs in healthy people indicating overfilling and inherent strength yet it is not obligatory to let blood nor to purge nor to induce emesis; rather it is sufficient for the patient to fast. For another person, it suffices to reduce one's food intake and for another it suffices to loosen the intestines[879] but not with an intestinal purgative. For another person, a bath is sufficient and for another only physical exercise [is needed] and for yet another only generalized[880] massaging. All these are very important matters. You, the perceptive reader, can decide[881] if we need an expert physician for these matters or whether we should rely[882] on one who has only seen matters in this art [of medicine but has no knowledge thereof].

33.   In the West[883] I saw a perfectly healthy[884] and well built young man who became afflicted with continuous fever. The physician bled him on the second day of the illness. After approximately fifty *zuz* of blood had been removed during the phlebotomy, the patient's spirit weakened.[885] The physician became frightened, ended the phlebotomy and instructed that the patient drink rose syrup and oxymel and be left alone[886] until the morning and then be fed appropriately as usual. But the patient died that night. Because of this case, there developed a discussion[887] between the physicians and the people. And one of the professors of medicine[888] under whom I studied told me as follows: "do you know the nature[889] of the mistake of that physician in phlebotomizing that patient". And I answered: "No, Master; do you also say that such treatment was a mistake?" And he laughed and said to me: "that patient was a pleasure-seeking person who loved to eat. As a result, the humors weakened the mouth of his

stomach[890] and[891] produced choleric juices. In such cases, Galen said that phlebotomy should not be used because the patient faints during the bloodletting. It is, therefore, more judicious to first strengthen the mouth of the stomach and to tighten it with external remedies after its emptying and to only resort to phlebotomy if he[892] has no other remedy. It is because he used phlebotomy before he strengthened the mouth of the stomach and he became alarmed and went away that the mouth of the stomach became even weaker, the humors flowed, the patient became overcome with faintness[893] and died". These are the words of my teacher.[894]

34. Says the author: Behold how many doubts[895] occur in these matters. For this reason I advise you not to rely on any [physician] who presents himself. To further underline the importance of this advice I think it worthwhile to cite the words of Galen in this matter according to which he said that one should phlebotomize a person suffering from continuous fever and remove blood without mercy until the patient faints. He qualified his remarks by saying that one should refrain from phlebotomizing for this type of fever and all the more so for other conditions. He [specifically] mentions [as contraindications to phlebotomy] the stomach in which there remains residue,[896] weakness of [the patient's] strength, old age,[897] [weak] constitution or [unfavorable] weather conditions at that time. He also states that one should not phlebotomize any person who produces acidity[898] at the mouth of the stomach or whose pylorus is weak and extremely sensitive. And he adds words to these statements as follows:

35. Concerning the bloodletting of which we spoke that one should let blood[899] until the patient faints to thereby extinguish the heat of the chronic fever which develops

from disturbed digestion[900] and assuages it, — often this [bloodletting] produces not insignificant harm if it is performed at the wrong time and in an inappropriate amount.

36. And I know two people whose deaths were caused by physicians because of fainting which occurred to them[901] at the time of the bloodletting and they died immediately.[902] Others did not die at once but perished later after they developed [severe] weakness of their strength and became flaccid. If they were phlebotomized[903] without developing weakness that sapped their strength, they did not die. Yet others suffered a change in their body constitution and developed a cold constitution which remained with them for the rest of their lives and could not be healed with any remedy;[904] all of this because of excessive bloodletting.[905] In some of these people that coldness [induced by bloodletting] is the cause for a change in their appearance and deterioratrion of the structure of their body such that they rapidly become ill and sick from the slightest cause. Eventually they develop near fatal asthenia[906] and severe weakness of the liver and the stomach and somnolence and flaccidity and paralysis.

37. Says the author: consider the results of bloodletting which is performed when not indicated or, even when needed, if performed to excess. I therefore correctly advise you[907] not to quickly place your care in the hands[908] of any physician whom you just happen to meet. In this matter, Galen has said that the same applies to the other emptyings of the body[909] if one rapidly performs them [at the wrong time or in excessive amounts].

38. The great medicines such as the theriac[910] and the Mithridates[911] and the Theodoritos[912] and similar medicines whose composition is complex and which the

physicians consider to be of great benefit are very powerful medicines.[913] One should not give any of them to drink to anyone and especially not to sick people except on the advice of a physician.

These [remedies], if used appropriately,[914] can cure many serious and dangerous illnesses on the same day. But if one is mistaken in the diagnosis and prescription[915] and uses them outside the proper indication, they can kill the patient or give rise to severe suffering.

The following incident occurred in the Occident[916] during the time of the Sultan Amrael Muselmin.[917] He once fell ill[918] but I did not learn the nature of his illness. He was [a little] older than twenty years of age and his body build was extremely powerful. It was wintertime and the city[919] where he became ill was the seat of the Occidental kings, the city of Marakesh. He recovered from his illness but had not yet regained his previous might and he performed [light] work like those convalescing from illness. The physicians were treating him with the usual regimens prescribed for convalescing patients; four of them were great sages in this art:[920] Abu Ali Ibn Zuhr,[921] Serapion,[922] Abu Al Chassan Ibn Kammiel of Saragossa the Israelite, and Abu Ayub Ibn Almulin of Seville the Israelite.[923] Because they saw that his body was pure but was not fully recovered and his digestion was weak and his fundamental [body] warmth was weak, and since he drank no wine,[924] the four [physicians] jointly decided to give him half a *zuz* of theriac to drink in order to revive his [body] warmth[925] and to strengthen his digestion and to restore all his natural [body] activities to their normal state, for these are the effects of the great theriac. They agreed to administer it to the patient during the last third of the night so that it not mix with food,[926] this being an indispensable condition [for success]. The physicians spent the night in the [royal] palace. And they came at the end of the night and brought the theriac sealed with the king's seal from the [royal] pharmacy and gave the patient the agreed-upon dose to drink. They returned to their quarters in the palace to [discuss] what foods to feed him. Three or four hours later, just before the morning prayers, a loud cry was heard in the palace.[927] And they called for the physicians to come [immediately] but [the Sultan] died before they arrived there or a moment after they arrived.

Abu Youssef the physician,[928] son of the aforementioned Abu Ayub, told me in the name of his father that the error was in the dose of the theriac for the patient could only tolerate one quarter *zuz* or one quarter *shekel*. And the minister Abu Bekr Ibn Abu Merwan Ibn Abu El'Ali told me that his father[929] Abu Merwan [Ibn Zuhr] thought that [his son] Abu El'Ali erred in the dose of the theriac saying that the death [of the Sultan Amrael Muselmin] was due to an insufficient dose. He should have received half a *shekel*.[930] I did not learn the [real] cause of [the Sultan's] death from any one of the physicians, as to whether the dose [of theriac] was insufficient or excessive. I asked every one of them individually[931] with the goal of benefitting [mankind] by learning and teaching.[932].

39. As time passed and I researched this and other matters, I found Galen stating things of which the following are the essentials. He said: all medications which are antidotes[933] for fatal drugs, if taken in an excessive dose, produce[934] very great harm to the body. For this reason, one should [only] use these medications in the proper dose[935] so that they not harm the body because of an excessive dose.[936]

40. Says the author:[937] it seems to me that those [physicians] who offered an explanation for that occurrence[938] imply

regret[939] that I did not cite evidence in the matter from the writings of a classical author. I have heard many things to explain the cause of that event but there is no benefit to mention them here. For the intent of this chapter has been accomplished and that is to warn patients not to hastily[940] take strong medications except on the advice of an eminent physician and [even then] with great caution [and only] if there is no other method [of cure] available.

41. The therapeutic method of the Egyptians[941] is as follows: they actually do not use medicines in most cases but prescribe a regimen for their patients in which the patient's nature is strengthened and he is cured or it is lost and he dies.[942] In general, I am in favor[943] of this approach. I will describe this method and then cite the reasons why I find it praiseworthy. It is clear to me from this method that they[944] were so cautious that they never used[945] most simple drugs and compounded medications but relied on a few commonly used mild drugs. When they needed to dilute or boil a thick humor, they employed weak medications which do not even attain the first level of warmth or at best a little of the second level. The strongest purgative that they prescribed is cassia fistula, rhubarb, agaricon and myrobalan. They did not use any type of hiera[946] such as hiera picra. Mostly their compounded medications consisted of apple juice, common flowering plants and customary fruit juices called *rab*.[947] Only rarely did they use one of the many beneficial medications such as the theriac or the electuary known as *zebid*.[948] If their intent was to add something they prescribed rose syrup. They never purged with a powerful [purgative] beverage. This is their method and I praise it for four reasons.

42. The first reason is the most important one and we have already mentioned it above[949] and that is the lack of knowledge of physicians. If he relies on a mild remedy and

if he is successful, he has done well. And if he errs and prescribes that which is inappropriate, the patient may not die but his illness becomes protracted. However, if he errs [by prescribing] a powerful medicine, the patient [invariably] dies.

43. The second reason is because their land is hot. Egypt is counted among the hot countries.[950] This matter therefore has a natural cause which is not part of this treatise. [A hot climate] causes weakening of one's strength and one should not use strong remedies in hot countries or in patients whose bodies are weak. Perhaps this was the reason why the theriac killed the young man[951] who was convalescing from his illness because potent drugs first overcome one's powers. If these [powers] are already weak and continue to diminish and dissipate and cannot be restored to their healthy state, [the potent drugs] easily overcome them.

44. The third reason is that most of their[952] illnesses are hot[953] because of the thinness of their humors and the leanness of their bodies.[954] These illnesses do not need strong medicines. It is well known that Hippocrates and Galen only treated acute illnesses with oxymel and barley porridge and their like.

45. The fourth reason is that they follow the rules commanded by [eminent] physicians and that is that anything that can be healed with diet alone should not be treated by any other means. If diet alone is insufficient,[955] administer mild medications. Anything that can be healed with a simple drug should not be treated with a compounded medication and [even then] one should select the least compounded remedy. If one is successful, one's goals have been achieved. All these things were commanded in general by the most eminent physicians. The Egyptians

follow this path in most instances. There is no doubt that sometimes they develop serious illnesses which require a strong remedy but they tarry in its use because they have no experience with such a potent remedy. For this reason their usual medication [applied in a case where a potent remedy is needed] produces no harm and their usual approach succeeds more often than it fails.[956]

46. However, that which we really reproach them for is their fear of giving patients the four-ingredient theriac[957] and the like to drink from the many beneficial medicinal potions or [their fear] of using a little pomegranate electuary[958] or that made from its mint[959] or their like from among the healing medications. [On the other hand], they utilize continuous bloodletting and remove large quantities of blood. And they give purgative drugs to drink at regular intervals as a method of medical practice[960] even to elderly people. All these things are obviously in error[961] and one should call attention thereto.

47. And I regularly observed in Egypt in relation to both prominent or ordinary people that only rarely would a single physician be appointed to care for the patient from the beginning to the end of his illness. In most cases, one would turn from physician to physician. Sometimes the patient might be treated by ten physicians for a single illness depending upon his wealth and one [physician] would not know about the other. The patient might deceive his physician saying: "I am relying on you" when in fact the patient or his attendant listen to the opinions of each of the doctors and he decides between them and chooses that which he perceives to be the best [advice]. In this manner he thinks that he can avoid and be spared physicians' errors. This method is associated with harmful effects and I will call your attention to them.

The first [problem] relates to the patient's own confusion since he does not know which [of his physicians] is correct. If he decides according to one of them, he [is nervous and] imagines that another may have the correct insight [into his illness].

The second [problem] relates to the confusion of the physician. For if he were retained to complete the treatment from beginning to end, he would remain with his therapeutic approach if it was clearly successful and, if not, would modify his treatment to another method.

The third [problem] lies in the mutual recrimination of the physicians[962]. Each one of them speaks badly of his colleague saying that the latter made an error.

The fourth [problem] lies in the laziness[963] of the physician and the weakness of his thinking and his acquiescence to [the opinion of] others. His reasoning is that if he errs, he will not be the only one blamed; and if he is correct, he will not be the only one to be credited. Therefore, he does not exert himself to apply his full knowledge because [he knows that] one is not relying on him alone.[964]

48. Rhazes said: he who is treated by many [physicians] risks suffering from[965] the combination of their errors.

49. Says the author: this is true if he is treated by each of them separately. But if all [the physicians] gather together [in consultation] as is done for kings and for wealthy people, and if they debate and deliberate and then render their opinion about what should be done [for the patient, the result] is helpful[966] and good. The patient benefits from their collective opinion because it is impossible for a single physician[967] to remember everything he learned, and this art [of medicine] is difficult for most scholars in terms of

the knowledge involved[968] which requires an exceptionally good memory. It may well happen that a physician cannot at the moment remember that which he needs [to treat] a given illness. But if there are many [physicians together in consultation] one reminds the other and assists him in completing his line of reasoning until they reach the perfect treatment plan to which they all agree.

And if one observes them quarelling, each one trying to excel[969] and boast and make known his [perceived] perfection to the patient and the deficiencies of his good and straightforward colleague, one should beware and dismiss them all lest the patient die if he only follows the advice of the victor. If they suffer from this disease,[970] they are all bad because righteousness is set aside even by the most perfect physician among them. I, therefore, advise you to abandon them all and to rely on the actions of nature. Our Sages[971] said: love and hate pervert judgment from the righteous path.[972]

50. Alexander Aphrodisius said: there are three causes for quarrels in [any] matter: first is the love of power and victory which prevents a person from seeing something as it really is; second is the profundity, fineness and essence of the matter which make it difficult to comprehend; and the third is the folly of the person and his lack of comprehension of that which is comprehensible.

51. Says the author[973]: behold, there is a fourth cause for argumentation [which should be added] to the three cited by Alexander. It is possible[974] that he did not mention it because it did not exist in his era or was not their custom. I refer to the force of habit in which a person remains attached to preconceived ideas and maintains his customary habits,[975] irrespective of whether these are in deeds or in ideas. For a person adopts[976] the ideas and

habits with which he was reared to the exclusion of others even if the latter are more correct. For example, a person may choose detrimental foods to which he is accustomed over wholesome foods to which he is not accustomed. This matter, however, is not within the scope of this treatise. My intent was to mention the first cause [for professional quarrelling] cited by Alexander since that was my intent in this chapter.

52. I have explained in this chapter how one can avoid[977] numerous harmful errors in the preservation of one's health and in the treatment of illnesses.

May the Lord with His kindness and truth lead us to that which is good in both worlds.[978] Praised be the Lord forever and ever.[979]

NOTES

1. Literally: Moses, son of Maimon, the Hebrew name of Moses Maimonides; Maimonides is his name in Greek.
2. Literally: tranquility or security.
3. Maimonides here indicates that his *Treatise on Asthma* was written at the request of a nobleman.
4. Muntner points out that Maimonides uses the same term in his *Commentary on the Aphorisms of Hippocrates* and that it is an abbreviation for the Hebrew phrase *ru'ach nefilim* or *ru'ach nefili* which means "short wind" or "cut off breathing". The term is also found in the Talmud, tractate *Bechorot* 44b where *Rashi* interprets it to mean "a spirit of madness". Here Muntner interprets *rinafli* to mean asthma or a related respiratory disorder.
5. Today the recognized stimuli that provoke asthma include allergens, aspirin and related substances, environmental and occupational factors, infections, exercise and emotional stress.
6. ?Neighboring affected organs.
7. Hebrew: *ashtot*. This word is found in Jeremiah 8:25.
8. Literally: years.
9. Literally: his conduct.
10. Literally: to make known the habits.
11. The signs and symptoms, clinical manifestations and treatment of asthma have been well described by medical authors.
12. Literally: hidden.
13. Literally: wondrous things.
14. Other physicians.
14a. Your Highness, the Sultan for whom Maimonides wrote this treatise.
15. Coryza or common cold or nasal drip.
16. The rainy season.
17. Literally: cooked.
18. Usually referring to a cathartic; here the term probably means an expectorant or decongestant.
19. By the phlegm being expelled through the nose.
20. Alternate version: feel faint.
21. Body temperament.
22. Muntner suggests that Maimonides is here referring to vasomotor rhinitis or allergic asthma.
23. Literally: heavy upon you.
24. Literally: to pass a razor over the head.
25. Literally: to increase turbans on it, i.e., the head.
26. Egypt here means Fostat or old Cairo because Alexandria is also part of Egypt.
27. Chapters not limited to the treatment of asthma but chapters which include rules of health in general.
28. The rules and regimens of health and the remedies for illnesses.
29. This treatise will also be helpful to humanity in general.

30. Literally: ways of foods.
31. I.e., asthma.
32. The purity of the air.
33. I.e., emotions.
34. Defecation, urination, vomiting, sweating, etc.
35. Alternate translation: bathing.
36. Perhaps the various signs and symptoms of this illness, i.e., asthma.
37. Alternate translation: last wills or testaments. Perhaps Maimonides advises that this concluding chapter of concise admonitions for the preservation of health and healing of illness should be as scrupulously followed as one would execute a last will or testament.
38. Literally: return.
39. Literally: trustworthy or reliable illnesses i.e., those illnesses which "reliably" exacerbate as seizures or attacks such as gout, arthritis, etc...
40. Intermittently and episodically and unpredictably like the eruption of a volcano.
41. Gout. Muntner's English version has "lumbago".
42. Literally: pain in the joints.
43. Kidney or gallbladder or urinary bladder stones.
44. See Maimonides' other medical writings where he discusses gout, arthritis, renal calculi and many more diseases. See especially, his *Medical Aphorisms* (trans. by Fred Rosner and Suessman Muntner, New York, Bloch for Yeshiva Univ. Press, 1973, 2 Volumes). Improved and revised edition by Fred Rosner published in 1990 by the Maimonides Research Institute, Haifa, Israel.
45. Literally: withheld.
46. Or number.
47. Literally: without being careful.
48. Literally: storm.
49. Literally: because of its creation.
50. Maimonides accepted the medieval concept relating to the four body humors: black bile (melancholy), red bile (blood), white bile (phlegm) and yellow bile. Disease was thought to occur secondary to an excess or insufficiency or maldistribution or faulty mixing of one or more of the humors. Health occurs when there is a normal equilibrium or homeostasis of the four body humors.
51. Literally: we find.
52. Alternate translation: the weak organ would be constantly ill.
53. Maimonides.
54. Literally: correct movements.
55. Literally: bad things.
56. Literally: virtues of the soul.
57. First because Galen stated them and second because Maimonides also tested them and found them efficacious.
58. But still recommended.
59. I.e., atmospheric purity.
60. Literally: movements of the soul.
61. Literally: movements of the body.

62. Of body wastes.
63. Alternate translation: washing.
64. Literally: diminish the semen (utilization).
65. Without the need to have children.
66. Literally: which adds, i.e., food which leaves much residue after its digestion.
67. Literally: rely on.
68. Literally: intermediate.
69. In the *Medical Aphorisms of Moses Maimonides* (see footnote 44) the author describes the various stages of digestion as follows:

     One can consider the assimilation of nutriments to occur conceptually in three stages. The *first* stage is digestion in the stomach which receives the digestate and adds it to the stomach substance until totally satiated. Simultaneously, a portion thereof rises to the liver. The *second* state is the transition to the intestines where it adds to the omentum and the liver substance. At this time, a small portion is distributed throughout the body. Consider at this time that the material that was added to the substance of the stomach in the *first* state has already become absorbed into and inseparable from its substance. The *third* stage is from the time one can consider the stomach to be nourished and that its substance has already assimilated that which it absorbed in the second stage. Meanwhile, the intestines and the liver digest and dilute that which was already added to their substance. The remainder passes to the other organs of the body and settles there. The digestion which occurs in the stomach is one type of alteration. Similarly also is the metabolism of the liver and the metabolism that occurs in every one of the organs. After this third metabolic phase, there is an additional metabolic phase, a fourth, which is called assimilation. The name assimilation is nothing more than another name for alimentation.

70. Literally: gasses.
71. Weak organs become even weaker.
72. I.e., soften or thin the thick, sticky residues.
73. The faulty or excessive thick, sticky humors.
74. Literally: thickening. Probably means that it produces thick body humors which then obstruct vessels or passages such as the bronchi.
75. Literally: the intent is.
76. Literally: closure and distress.
77. Literally: winds.
78. Openings through which the food passes.
79. Literally: or.
80. Alternate translation: vaporize, turn into gas.
81. Maimonides.
82. Hebrew: *tzava'ah*, literally: last will and testament. See note 37 above.
83. Literally: thickening foods.
84. Asthma.
85. The sultan for whom Maimonides wrote this treatise.

86. Literally: that which empties the body, i.e., a normal or reducing diet.
87. To become extremely lean or thin.
88. Arabic: brain.
89. Literally: things.
90. Literally: afflict.
91. Phlegm.
92. Literally: rely on.
93. Literally: thickness.
94. Alternate version: with.
95. I.e., white and pure finely ground flour.
96. Or moistened.
97. It is not clear whether the Hebrew word *bishul* meaning ripening or cooking here refers to the rising bread in the oven or to the bread in the eater's stomach where it is well "cooked". i.e., digested.
98. Alternate translation: all grains or seeds.
99. Hebrew: *morsan*, coarse bran. See the Talmud, tractate *Shabbat*, folio 125.
100. Literally: ground to an intermediate grinding.
101. The sultan.
102. Crushed seed kernels (Proverbs 27:22); barley crushed in a mortar; groats.
103. Spelt kernels or wheat kernels or barley kernels or cleft wheat barley. The word *targis* is found in the Talmud, tractate *Machshirin*, folio 6b.
104. See the Talmud, tractate *Pesachim*, folio 39b.
105. Literally: threads or cords.
106. Macaroni, spaghetti, vermicelli, etc.
107. Of the phlegm, thus aggravating asthma or precipitating an attack.
108. Cakes.
109. Perhaps tarts.
110. Such as strudel.
111. Literally: badly, i.e., inadequately.
112. Literally: cane honey.
113. See note 50 above.
114. Literally: breads.
115. Literally: closed.
116. Literally: heart.
117. Literally: pure or innocent.
118. This sentence is totally omitted in Muntner's English translation. In a footnote in his Hebrew version, Muntner points out that this statement is erroneous since unleavened bread is very efficacious against flatulence.
119. Maimonides.
120. Literally: swelling.
121. Vicia faba.
122. Garden beans.
123. White beans; phaseolus, dolichos, vigna.
124. Cicer arietenum.
125. Oryza sativa. See the Talmud, tractate *Demai*, Chapter 1:1.

126. Allium porrum.
127. See note 74 above.
128. Rather use calf or fowl meat.
129. See note 74 above.
130. Literally: do not approach them.
131. Produce thick humors.
132. Difficult to digest.
133. Hazel hen.
134. See Talmud, tractate *Nedarim*, folio 50b.
135. The Sultan for whom Maimonides wrote this treatise.
136. Alternate translation: clear or clean.
137. Literally: praised.
138. Salt water or ocean fish.
139. Literally: pieces and thinness.
140. Literally: which is salted from close by. ? fish which live in lightly salted waters as opposed to the heavily salted oceans.
141. Sheep or goats.
142. Literally: in the house.
143. See note 135 above.
144. Alternate translation: haunches.
145. The head, anterior extremities and chest.
146. Asthma.
147. During its preparation.
148. Literally: praised.
149. These have little nutritional value.
150. Beta vulgaris; also mangold.
151. In a note in his Hebrew edition, Muntner states that this term includes buds of all types of grasses and trees and especially cabbage sprouts. See the Talmud, tractate *Nedarim*, folio 53.
153. Apium graveolens; also celery.
154. Mentha pulegium; pennyroyal.
155. Summer savory, origanum.
156. Nasturtium.
157. Raphanus sativus.
158. Having little nutritional value.
159. Lactuca sativa.
160. Armoles hortensis or atriplex.
161. Moluchia, Malva Corchorus olitorius.
162. Coloquinthe Cucurbita Pepo; also pumpkin.
163. Literally: bad.
164. Fleshy plants.
165. Arum colocassia. Muntner cites a discussion of this plant in the Jerusalem Talmud, tractate *Nedarim*, folio 40.
166. Turnip; Brassica napus. Muntner cites the Talmud, tractate *Uktzin*, Chapter 1:2, where Rav Hai Gaon interprets this plant to be long radish.
167. Pastinaca agrestis.
168. Brassica oleracea; also cauliflower.
169. Solanum melongena; also eggplant.

170. Brassica rapa. See the Talmud, tractate *Kilayim*, Chapter 1:3.
171. Literally: empty.
172. Alternate translation: in any form (or amount) whatever.
173. Literally: liquid, i.e., moist or fresh or juicy.
174. Amygdalus persica; resembles almonds.
175. Sometimes substituted for prunes.
176. Morus.
177. Cucumis sativus.
178. Cornichon; small cucumber.
179. Hebrew: *rotev*. See the Talmud tractate *Uktzin*, Chapter 2:2.
180. Literally: swelling.
181. Literally: add to the difficulty of digestion.
182. Literally: does not harm me.
183. Porridge.
184. Ruta graveolens, peganum.
185. Pennyroyal, colomint.
186. Cuminum cyminum.
187. Literally: empties.
188. The sultan for whom Maimonides wrote this treatise.
189. Aternate version: cooked.
190. Cydonia vulgaris.
191. Literally: prisoners.
192. The fruit of zizyphus spina christi.
193. Crataegus azarolus. Hebrew: *Azardin*. See Talmud, tractate *Berachot* 40b.
194. Literally: cooking.
195. Literally: sticking or burning.
196. Literally: tube of the lung. ? trachea.
197. Dill. Anethum foeniculi.
198. Pistacia palaestina; terebinth.
199. Literally: until you learn to eat them.
200. Alternate translation: empty, i.e., rid the body of.
201. Phlegm.
202. Alternate version: open all obstructions in the bronchi.
203. ? Depression.
204. Pinus pinea.
205. Literally: hearts, i.e., seeds.
206. Literally: wheat milk.
207. Literally: compounding.
208. Literally: explained.
209. Ruta graveolus; peganum.
210. Rice. Muntner claims *barang* is a copyist's error since the original Arabic text has *asfidabag* which is lactuva sativa.
211. Arabic: *zabiya*.
212. Pour boiling water on the meat.
213. Literally: sour wine.
214. *Sumkiya*.
215. Literally: praised.

216. I.e., it dries the body.
217. Asthma.
218. Literally: burning at the mouth of the stomach, i.e., heartburn.
219. It is unclear who "they" refers to here; ? physicians.
220. Raisins.
221. Produces jaundice by increasing the yellow bile.
222. Literally: harms or damages.
223. Impedes expectoration or phlegm.
224. The ingredients in this dish or therapeutic preparation.
225. Literally: compounded (dish).
226. An unseasoned dish without salt.
227. A type of soup.
228. The meat recommended in the previous paragraph.
229. Carthamus tinctorius; safflower.
230. Alternate translation: autumn.
231. The Arabic has "mint".
232. Foeniculum.
233. Literally: hearts; i.e., pits or kernels or stones.
234. Alternate version: chicken soup.
235. A Moroccan dish.
236. Muries.
237. Meaning unclear?
238. Literally: crumbs; perhaps refers to the hog's onions.
239. Literally: vinegar.
240. Muntner quotes Asaph and Maimonides who consider the *askil* to be the wild onion and Dioscorides who cites the scylla maritima. Here, according to Muntner, it refers to the small hog's onion.
241. A small measure.
242. Damascus mustard; sinapis orientalis.
243. Literally: first by first.
244. Literally: sour wine.
245. Literally: things.
246. The body constitution of the sultan for whom Maimonides wrote this treatise.
247. Literally: I see all this.
248. The sultan.
249. Sharp or acrid taste.
250. In Arabic countries sharp spicy foods such as peppers, mustard, paprika, cumin and their like were commonly consumed.
251. Brassica oleracea. Arabic: *kirfaz* meaning cinnamon and *karawiya* meaning caraway.
252. Nardostachys, Valeriana tuberosa, Valeriana spica.
253. Pistacia lenticus; Arabic: *muscat.*
254. Hebrew: *gad.* See Exodus 16:31.
255. Literally: so that its warming not be apparent, i.e., add a very small amount of these spices to give the food a taste but insufficient to make their sharpness perceptible.
256. Zingiber, zerumbet.

257. Flores caryophylli aromatica.
258. Folia pini cedri. In Arabic: *tanbul*, betel leaves.
259. Or liquification (of humors and foods).
260. Literally: cook (the food).
261. Cakes and pastries.
262. Sorbitio; a dish made of dates.
263. A wheat paste mixed with meat.
264. Literally: obstruct.
265. A mixture of cane sugar and sweet almonds.
266. The amount and type of food and other specific remedies are prescribed according to the individual person's constitution and needs.
267. When the weather becomes hot.
268. Literally: when the cold becomes a little stronger.
269. Tympany.
270. Literally: activities.
271. Literally: to let the food sink from the stomach.
272. Literally: placing it.
273. Literally: remove his hands.
274. Before complete satiation or oversatiation.
275. Literally: habit or conduct.
276. Literally: measure.
277. Literally: reaches under the esophagus.
278. Alternate translation: churning or turning stomach.
279. Literally: stinging at the mouth of the stomach.
280. Muntner suggests the reference here is to aerophagia (?with gastric dilation) or pseudo-angina pectoris.
281. Literally: instructed or commanded.
282. A single food is best for digestion.
283. Literally: harm.
284. Literally: thick.
285. Literally: thin.
286. I.e., has a laxative effect.
287. Constipating or contracting substance.
288. Literally: I have.
289. Eating a single dish at a meal.
290. Literally: strengthens.
291. Alternate translation: increases for each food consumed.
292. Literally: and this is greater than all.
293. Literally: one should rely on it.
294. Literally: commanded.
295. Literally: because of its great esteem.
296. Literally: just as.
297. Literally: perform hard exercises.
298. Literally: better than all things.
299. Maimonides.
300. Literally: it should be clear to you.
301. Literally: entering a bathhouse.
302. Literally: offense, trespass.

303. Literally: is visible to the eye.
304. Literally: occurrences.
305. Abdominal distention; ?tympany.
306. Heartburn; ?gastritis.
307. ?Constipation.
308. Diarrhea.
309. Asthenia; ?impotence.
310. Literally: obstruction of the intellect.
311. Thoughts secondary to black bile.
312. ?Urinary retention; ?constipation. Muntner suggests: spastic ileus.
313. Nephritis.
314. Hepatitis.
315. Arthritis.
316. Literally: confusion of the body; ?generalized malaise.
317. Literally: storminess of the body; shaking chills or convulsions.
318. Maimonides.
319. Literally; noble or princely organ of his organs.
320. Muntner translates: I do not know.
321. The sultan for whom Maimonides wrote this treatise.
322. Literally: decree or command.
323. Literally: for a short time.
324. Literally: for a long time. Muntner states that Galen is not correct.
325. Maimonides.
326. Galen.
327. Literally: no matter which way.
328. Literally: clean.
329. Literally: it is proper in this matter to rely on the emptiness (or cleanliness) of the stomach.
330. Literally: heat or coldness.
331. Alternate translation: heating.
332. After his stomach is empty.
333. Literally: limit or boundary.
334. As a criterion of when to eat next.
335. Such as nausea, eructation and heartburn.
336. Literally: the cold season.
337. Literally: heat.
338. Alternate translation: is advanced or delayed.
339. Alternate translation: autumn.
340. Literally: these things happen many times.
341. Muntner explains that Maimonides ate only one meal a day except for the Sabbath when he ate the three prescribed meals. At night, he ate tidbits so as not to fall asleep on an empty stomach.
342. To expel the bad humors.
343. Alternate translation: soft boil.
344. Winter.
345. Wine is prohibited to Moslems by religious law; see also beginning of next chapter.
346. Literally: Ishmaelites.

347. Literally: bad and hard.
348. Asthma.
349. Literally: fundamental warmth.
350. Since your Highness is prohibited from using it, i.e., a wine-containing remedy.
351. Alternate version: blacken.
352. Mead.
353. Arabic: shows the highest degree of excellence, based on theoretical reasoning.
354. The last phrase is missing in the Arabic manuscript.
355. Or linseed.
356. Until they soften.
357. Literally: selected.
358. Literally: weak.
359. Literally: first first.
360. Borago officinalis.
361. Mentha.
362. Literally: and that which I see.
363. Adiantum capillus veneris.
364. Anethum graveolens; dill. See the Talmud tractates *Peah* 3:2; *Maaserot* 5:4; and *Kilayim* 1:2.
365. Arundo.
366. Balsam of Pistacia lentiscus.
367. Valeriana tuberosa. See tractate *Shabbat*, folio 87.
368. Crocus sativus.
369. Literally: time after time.
370. Made of roses, sugar and water.
371. Literally: bubbles or boils; ?undergoes fermentation.
372. Mix or blend or temper.
373. Literally: parts.
374. Mentha aquatica; also mentha pulegium or mentha sativa.
375. Or shortly after the meal.
376. Literally: separates.
377. Your Highness' habit of drinking water with meals.
378. Literally: free from a change in odor.
379. River or lake or spring waters as opposed to salty ocean water.
380. Could Maimonides be speaking of the sterilization of water to destroy bacteria and other microorganisms?
381. Liquiritia glabria.
382. Or mastic.
383. Literally: enumerated.
384. Literally: connects.
385. Literally: increases.
386. Literally: reddens the countenance.
387. Literally: hot or heating.
388. Perhaps angina pectoris.
389. Sepsis.
390. Muntner points out that the original version has dropsy or ascites.

391. Literally: heat.
392. Literally: putrefaction.
393. See chapter 1, section 3 where Maimonides lists them as follows: air, food and beverages, emotions, body exercise, rest, sleeping and waking, evacuation and retention.
394. Emotions.
395. Atmosphere.
396. Literally: putrefaction.
397. Literally: good water; i.e., perfumed water to give a good scent and to cool the atmosphere.
398. These moisten and cool the air.
399. For example by using a fan.
400. I.e., cold.
401. Your Highness, the sultan for whom Maimonides wrote this treatise.
402. Coryza or dripping nose. Muntner translates: urine stimulants; such translation seems out of place within the context of this paragraph.
403. Literally: movements of the soul.
404. Literally: shortness of spirit.
405. Literally: raise.
406. I.e., move.
407. Literally: broaden the soul.
408. Literally: avoidance of falling into them.
409. A dietary regimen.
410. Literally: professions; specialties, occupations.
411. Muntner interprets this phrase to refer to psychology.
412. Literally: will be saved more from.
413. Literally: activities.
414. Ordinary people.
415. Literally: movement of his soul.
416. Literally: strength and weakness of the heart.
417. Literally: mockery, derision, laughter.
418. Fleeting fancies. Vanity of vanities (Ecclesiastes 1:1 and Isaiah 2:18).
418a. The sultan for whom Maimonides wrote this treatise on asthma.
419. Literally: toiling, working.
420. From asthma.
421. Literally: a regimen of health.
422. Muntner interprets: do not mourn excessively for the dead.
423. Excretion of body fluids and other wastes through vomiting, defecation, urination, perspiration, etc.
424. Bad humors or an excess of humors.
425. Literally: his nature should be loose.
426. Constipation.
427. Arabic: and a purgative must be taken.
428. Abu Merwan Ibn Zuhr, also known as Avenzoar, famous Arabic physician frequently cited by Maimonides in his medical writings.
429. Tamarind.
430. Arabic: Chinese rhubarb.
431. Maimonides.

432. Arabic: *kurtum* which Muntner interprets to mean the punica granatum. Muntner also translates: wild growing olives.
433. Cournouiller in French and *Lubab saghir* in Arabic.
434. Carthamus tinctorius. See tractates *Shabbat*, folio 110 and *Chullin*, folio 47.
434a. Literally: edible salt.
435. Literally: until it gathers.
436. Literally: and further.
437. Arabic: of which half a *litre*.
438. Arabic: *samgh el butm*; terebinth resin.
439. Alternate translation: it heals.
440. Literally:; time after time.
441. Beta vulgaris. See tractates *Terumot* 10:11 and *Uktzin* 1:4.
442. Literally: waters.
443. To preserve the warmth of this remedy.
444. Literally: broth or dish.
445. Cordia myxa; Muntner also has aristolochia rotunda.
446. Acacia aegyptica; Muntner also has amomum and quotes the Arabic text: with licorice roots and marsh mallow.
447. Diarrhea.
448. Rhus coriaria.
449. Alternate translation: unripe dates.
450. Literally: return nature to its habit.
451. Constipating.
452. Literally: whose custom is to heal, i.e., general practitioners.
453. Globularia alypi or ipomoea turpethum.
454. Convolvulus scammonia.
455. Clysters.
456. *Ibid.*
457. Mucosa.
458. Sodium bicarbonate.
459. See tractate *Shabbat*, folio 155.
460. Trigonella foenum graecum.
461. Arabic: red beets.
462. See I Samuel 14:27.
463. Literally: the fever of blight, i.e., phthisis or tuberculosis. Alternate translation: hectic fever.
464. Literally: permanent.
465. Several phases of digestion were described by ancient physicians. See note 69 above.
466. Feces and urine.
467. Literally: its gasses. i.e., the feces are mixed with pneuma and transformed into gasses.
468. Literally: is part of the regimen of health.
469. Asthma.

470. It seems unusual for Maimonides to cite Divine Providence. Muntner explains that human beings, unlike ruminating animals, have a single stomach and therefore need the biliary system to dissolve phlegm and other stomach contents. Otherwise diseases would occur. Vomiting is one method to expel superfluities from the stomach which cannot be digested. Ruminants, on the other hand, continues Muntner, cannot distinguish between good and bad food and therefore require a "second" stomach to allow them to digest that which was not digested in the "first" stomach.
471. Literally: Galen stated things and these are his words.
472. Literally: cleanse or purify.
473. I.e., injurious to health.
474. But for vomiting they are useful.
475. Mouldy bread or fruit steeped in vinegar.
476. Muntner translates: leeks.
477. Sour milk or buttermilk or the like.
478. Literally: sections. This meaning of this phrase is unclear. The Latin version reads: *et non fuerint humores inviscati in suis pelliculis.*
479. The sultan for whom Maimonides wrote this treatise.
480. Literally: in the manner known to us.
481. Alternate translation: and (add) an amount of nuts.
482. Anethum graveolens.
483. Cucumis melo.
484. Prunus armeniaca.
485. Allium porrum.
486. Hebrew: *Grissin shel pul*, a term frequently found in the Talmud, e.g., tractates *Niddah,* Chapter 9 and *Machshirin,* Chapter 5, etc.
487. Literally: half the day.
488. Literally: in the bathhouse.
489. Literally: until hunger has become strong over him.
490. Chicken soup. Muntner states that the Arabic *zirbag* refers to a mixture of sugar, almonds and vinegar.
491. A beverage made from vinegar and honey.
492. Muntner also translates plantago psyllium.
493. Scilla; bulbus maritima.
494. Literally: it emptied a good emptying.
495. See note 69.
496. Literally: for this amount.
497. That of lemon juice.
498. Literally: tendons, i.e., joints.
499. Plethora.
500. Literally: at known times.
501. Literally: step by step.
502. Alternate translation: The practice of bloodletting and purgation is already outmoded (literally: has ceased).
503. Literally: one should reduce it as much as possible.
504. Your Highness.
505. Literally: smokes or vapors.

506. Literally: cooking.
507. Literally: step by step.
508. Literally: until nature supports it and becomes convinced.
509. Literally: preserving health.
510. Different people have different habits.
511. Asthma.
512. Physicians.
513. Literally: your thoughts should be.
514. Arabic text has: a bath should only be taken on an empty stomach.
515. Literally: when you leave.
516. Literally: cook.
517. Literally: by themselves.
518. Maimonides.
519. Literally: the night sleep which prevails and is accepted.
520. Literally: him, i.e., your Highness.
521. Literally: the desire therewith.
522. Literally: the later (physicians) state.
523. Literally: limit or fence.
524. Literally: straightens.
525. Arms and legs.
526. Maimonides' *Regimen of Health* or *Regimen Sanitatis*. See the introductory paragraph entitled "The Medical Writings of Moses Maimonides" in this book.
527. Literally: mention.
528. Literally: their illness becomes stormy and explosive.
529. Between attacks of the disease.
530. Arabic text: and internal warmth.
531. Literally: emitted.
532. Coitus.
533. Literally: from the standpoint of hygiene of the body.
534. Arabic text: decline in mental power.
535. Jaundice or pallor.
536. Literally: destruction of the light of the eyes.
537. Literally: their soul widens.
538. Literally: and said things in the following terms.
539. Asthma.
540. Literally: at the time one exists from the bath.
541. A laxative.
542. Sweat and semen.
543. Serious or chronic.
544. Literally: begun with.
545. Asthma.
546. The Latin manuscript has: *aegritudo instrumentalis*. In medieval times distinction was made between *evarim* (literally: organs) or *kelim keliyim* (vital organs) such as the brain, heart and liver and *kelim mitdamiyim* (secondary organs) such as the arms, legs, nose, etc.
547. Literally: every.
548. Your Highness.

549. From a rubefacient.
550. Maimonides' repeated use of the word brain probably refers to the mind or intellect.
551. Literally: whose strengths differ, i.e., sometimes they cool and sometimes they warm the brain.
552. Literally: prevented.
553. The Arabic text has: only the thin juices dissolve while the turbid ones solidify.
554. The remedies.
555. Literally: the thing which descends.
556. Arabic: hot and thin.
557. Literally: minces it or cuts it up.
558. Your Highness.
559. Literally: syllogisms.
560. Literally: who does not know the paths of syllogisms.
561. Your Highness.
562. Literally: of others.
563. Asthma.
564. Literally: the pious physicians or the followers (i.e., disciples) of physicians.
565. Your Highness.
566. In the next chapter.
567. Literally: alone.
568. Literally: the days of Nissan; approximately April.
569. If you feel bloated, take liquid medications (?purgatives) twice a year.
570. Literally: improve your conduct.
571. Literally: darkened it.
572. Literally: abbreviated or shortened or cut off.
573. Literally: step by step.
574. Literally: time after time. Muntner translates: use emetics, one after the other.
575. So as not to fall. Literally: one should lean on each side.
576. Perhaps Maimonides means unboiled water.
577. See note 36 above.
578. Liquiritia.
579. Altherea, malva.
580. Lingua bovis, Borago officinalis.
581. Adiantum capilli veneris. In Arabic: *kuzbarat bir*; also Mentha pulegia.
582. Anethum foeniculum.
583. Rosewater syrup.
584. Mentha pulegia.
585. Hebrew: *ethrog*, i.e., citrus.
586. Oxymel, a mixture of honey and vinegar.
587. Thick secretions or phlegm.
588. Ocimum basilicum. The Arabic text here has: liquorice.
589. Mentha pulegium.
590. Lavendula stoechas.
591. Arabic: *attarun*; druggists or pharmacists.

592. Satureia hortensis. Arabic: *kanturiyum*; not found in the Hebrew manuscript.
593. Thymus capitatus.
594. Liquiritia.
595. Marubium vulgare. Arabic: *asl susan,* susan roots.
596. Rubio tinctorum.
597. Literally: balsam and its tree.
598. Valeriana tuberosa.
599. Mentha silvestris.
600. Anthemus nobilis and Pyrethrum parthenium.
601. Sutureia hortensis.
602. Literally: drippings from the head, i.e., rhinitis.
603. Nasal secretion.
604. Mentha pulegium.
605. Bugloss.
606. Fresh.
607. Nenuphar; Nymphaea lotus coerulea.
608. Cucumis sativus.
609. Eruca sativa. Muntner also has Curcuma longo, Chelodinium majus and Cuscuta.
610. Cordia myxa.
611. Semptervivum arboreum.
612. Whatever is in season.
613. Violet.
614. Asthma.
615. Ceterach officinarum or scale fern.
616. Has a scientific basis or is based on scientific reasoning.
617. Literally: custom.
618. Literally: accepted.
619. Literally: lickings, i.e., potions taken by the spoonful rather than the glassful.
620. Bulbus scillae.
621. Mentha silvestris and mentha aquatica.
622. Thymus capitatus.
623. Iris.
624. Fennel.
625. Balsamodendron.
626. Rubia tinctorium; saffran.
627. Literally: upon which it is appropriate for you (i.e., Your Highness) to rely.
628. Pinus cedrus or pinces pinea. Perhaps also Acacia nilotica.
629. Marrubium vulgare.
630. Liquiritia, glykyrrhiza.
631. Literally: almond hearts.
632. Creme of sugar or sugar icing.
633. Literally: burned.
634. I.e., until it develops the consistency of a potion or electuary.
635. Meaning unclear. Arabic: *aspargali*; perhaps it means quinces.

636. Ocimum basilicum or Adiantum capillus veneris.
637. For all conditions for which it is administered.
638. Literally: completely cooked.
639. Literally: lick it.
640. Than the potion made with grape juice.
641. Astragalus.
642. Dried resin from acacia trees.
643. Literally: first, first.
644. *Ibid.*
645. Alternate translation: cucumber seeds.
646. Arabic text has: and she was unmarried.
647. Of asthma.
648. Between attacks.
649. Muntner points out that this passage is mentioned by Nathan Falkira in his book *Tzarey Haguf.*
650. Literally: without weight.
651. Ocimum basilicum.
652. Mentha.
653. Alternate translation: And I removed it (from the fire).
654. Urtica urens.
655. Semen lini.
656. Lilium candidum.
657. Inula helenium.
658. Radix valeriana.
659. Raphanus sativus.
660. Marrubium.
661. Scolopendrium.
662. Seseli tortuosum.
663. Literally: drugs.
664. Arabic text has eighteen.
665. Scientific considerations.
666. Literally: what I have observed by testing.
667. Your Highness.
668. Literally: constantly.
669. Medicinas appondenas supra caput.
670. Pinus pinea; also Valeriana celtica.
671. Platanus orientalis; Santalum album.
672. Arabic: *Sunbul*; valeriana.
673. Literally: water.
674. Storax.
675. Famous physicians.
676. Endives.
677. Literally: face of the head.
678. Muntner translates: *before* leaving the bath.
679. Literally: constantly.
680. Literally: the later ones.
681. Literally: it has been truly tested.
682. Liquid storax.

683. Dill.
684. Auripigment.
685. Gum arabic.
686. Olibanum.
687. Resin of Ferula galbaniflua or Lacrima ferula syriacae.
688. Mangold.
689. Sodium bicarbonate.
690. Mentha silvestris and saturei.
691. Literally: if there are winds.
692. Caraway seeds.
693. Sagapenum.
694. Pannicum miliaceum; opoponax.
695. Desiccated substance of the abdominal glands of the castor fiber.
696. Alternate translation: warm.
697. During the summer.
698. Literally: prevented.
699. Phlegm.
700. A ready-made electuary composed of various plants.
701. Fungus laricis.
702. Ipomea turpethum.
703. Arabic: *kathira*; astragalus.
704. Arabic text adds; in honey water.
705. Your Highness.
706. Of asthma.
707. Lilium candidum.
708. Marrubium.
709. Arabic: *kathira*, see note 703 above.
710. Ecballum eleterium.
711. Artemisia absinthium.
712. The Arabic text adds: an eighth *zuz* each of convolvus scammonia and mastic, and half a *zuz* of blue bdellium.
713. Cuscuta epithymum.
714. Ferula sagapenum.
715. Urtica urens.
716. Polypolium vulgare.
717. Arabic: *alkam,* wild cucumber.
718. Literally: hearts.
719. Apium graveolens.
720. Asthma.
721. Alternate translation: from above.
722. Perhaps its shell or its leaves.
723. Literally: cast on it.
724. Zizyphus vulgaris.
725. There are several types of myroblalan, e.g., emblici, indici, etc...
726. Bouglosson or Anchusa italica.
727. Lavendula.
728. Lemon-like fruit; satureia hortensis.
729. To purge.

730. Literally: things.
731. Literally: elders, i.e., famous Spanish and Moroccan physicians.
732. Literally: a large gate.
733. Literally: countries.
734. Helleborus album.
735. Hydromel.
736. Sinapsis.
737. Bolus alba. Alternate translation: aromatic borax.
738. A solid measure.
739. Literally: a regimen of health.
740. Alternate translation: last wills or testaments. See note 37 above.
741. One's primary concern should be the provision of fresh air, clean water and a healthy diet.
742. Breaths.
743. Literally: vapor, gas.
744. Hebrew: *sirayon*, literally: armor, ? thorax. Muntner suggests that *sirayon* refers to the pulmonary arteries.
745. Literally: spirit of the soul.
746. Smog.
747. Literally: subject.
748. Literally: comparison and mixture.
749. The translation of this statement of Galen is uncertain or unclear, Muntner also provides the Latin version: *Inquit Galenus: "Consideratio in substantia aeris quam contrahit homo in sua aspiratione, est ut it fine [sine?] temperantia [e] ab omni re quae ipsum coinquinat."* The thrust of the statement is to advise us to pay attention to the quality of the air which we inhale and to insure that no harmful or malodorous substances be mixed in with it.
750. I.e., pneuma.
751. Alternate translation: in the quality of the pneuma.
752. Literally: functions of the soul.
753. For fear of marshes and ponds with mosquitoes and other insects. Alternatively: where there is little rainfall, i.e., a dry area.
754. Suburbs.
755. Muntner translates: southern.
756. Literally: enter.
757. Literally: nature is softened a little.
758. Literally: nature becomes dried.
759. Literally: pious.
760. Literally: making it harder for nature.
761. By being prodded with a stick.
762. Literally: moved.
763. I.e., the natural urge to defecate.
764. Normal bowel activity may be impeded by giving constipating medications for mild, otherwise asymptomatic, diarrhea.
764a. Literally: looseness or weakness (of the bowels).
765. Literally: lazy.
766. Let nature heal itself.

767. Arabic physician (870-950 C.E.) frequently cited by Maimonides.
768. Literally: activity.
769. Literally: seeds.
770. Capsizes.
771. Muntner translates: *people* exert themselves to get rid of the disorder... I believe that Maimonides meant that *nature* attempts to get rid of the disorder.
772. Famous Persian physician (850-923 C.E:) frequently quoted by Maimonides in his medical writings.
773. This aphorism is also quoted by Maimonides in his *Regimen of Health*, Chapter 4:6.
774. The physician.
775. In a footnote, Muntner states that this passage is rather obscure and its translation tentative. Its Latin version is likewise not easily understood. It reads as follows: *Ex verbo huius viri perfecti in arte sua etiam sciri potest, quoniam non indigere medico magis est quam indigere ipso cum facta fuerit comparatio in universis aegritudinibus, et hoc quando fuerit ille ordinatus sciens substantare naturam et iuvare ipsam non quod ponat ipsam in confusionem et eam deponat a sua consuetidine et ordine convenienti.*
776. How many times.
777. Rectal hemorrhage.
778. Gastritis, heartburn; ? peptic ulcer.
779. Literally: heart trouble; ? angina pectoris. See Lamentations 3:65.
780. Literally: these previous matters.
781. Literally: beginning causes.
782. Muntner interprets the cause of death to be septicemia.
783. Literally: blind their eyes.
784. Literally: small matter.
785. Literally: softens nature.
786. Literally: extinguishes their fire.
787. Literally: enter the bathhouse.
788. Infection?
789. Literally: filled.
790. Arabic: humanities.
791. Arabic: religious science.
792. Alternate translation: and he develops novel ideas.
793. Difficult or far-reaching problems.
794. Literally: brings near.
795. Here meaning the theory of medical practice.
796. Literally: man's practice or application.
797. Juice of Cucumis agrestis.
798. The Hebrew version here differs somewhat from the Arabic original.
799. The Hebrew text here adds the word *chafifah* which literally means washing one's hair. The meaning here is unclear.
800. When I was practicing medicine with other physicians.
801. Literally: known for their medicines.
802. Literally: this thing happened.

803. Literally: when I wished to feed the patient with one of the powerful nutriments.
804. Literally: thought.
805. Maimonides probably means that Hippocrates witnessed such therapeutic errors rather than Hippocrates having committed them.
806. Medicine.
807. Literally: saw or observed.
808. Literally: teachings or instructions or indications.
809. Diligence and even reversal of a decision in case of doubt so as to avoid unnecessary harm to the patient.
810. Literally: the length of its part.
811. See my English edition published by the Maimonides Research Institute, Haifa, Israel, 1987. From this statement, it is evident that Maimonides wrote his *Commentary on the Aphorisms of Hippocrates* before he wrote his *Treatise on Asthma.*
812. Literally: and if I prefaced all this for you.
813. Your Highness.
814. Literally: soul.
815. Literally: choicest.
816. I.e., more frequent.
817. Muntner has an alternate translation: in his treatise on natural science.
818. Muntner translates: the nature of the patient both when he is healthy and ill.
819. Your Highness.
820. Literally: our conduct or management or direction.
821. Maimonides here alludes to preventive medicine.
822. Literally: it is near in my eyes.
823. I.e., from a physician.
824. Literally: the masses of extant (physicians), i.e., most physicians are imperfect.
825. Literally: places or sites.
826. Alternate translation: poor person or beggar.
827. Literally: do not reach the results which result.
828. Literally: the matter is equal.
829. Literally: righteous or straightforward.
830. Alternate translation: the help.
831. Literally: received by the body.
832. Maimonides.
833. Literally: complete. i.e., skillful, experienced and ethical.
834. Literally: believe.
835. Your Highness.
836. Literally: in my eyes.
837. Maimonides' humility is clearly evident in this statement.
838. Literally: a second time.
839. Literally: teach.
840. Literally: I testify to the truth of these things.
841. Literally: brought.
842. Your Highness.

843. Literally: to acquit myself.
844. Literally: to that which I wished (to explain).
845. Literally: experimentaion, i.e., experience.
846. Literally: their minds are guided.
847. Muntner's Hebrew text has the words "in western countries" in parentheses.
848. See Proverbs 21:24.
849. Literally: found.
850. Literally: tested things.
851. The people.
852. The medical quacks.
853. Alternate translation: possessed proven remedies.
854. Literally: things.
855. Literally: lessen.
856. A single physician (?medical quack) cannot possibly draw valid conclusions from a single experiment on a single patient but should rely on the collective experience of many physicians over many centuries.
857. The first aphorism of Hippocrates. See Maimonides' *Commentary on the Aphorisms of Hippocrates* (F. Rosner, translator). Maimonides Research Institute, Haifa, Israel, 1987.
858. Literally: Cause people to err.
859. Literally: which had no sign.
860. Literally: their deficiency.
861. Literally: without wisdom or without science.
862. Literally: one can find a person.
863. Literally: has no regular proficiency in the practice of medicine.
864. Was not an apprentice to a practicing physician.
865. Literally: looked or watched.
866. Muntner provides the Latin translation of this important rule: *quoriam medicus non curabat speciem aegritudinis sed individuum ipsius.*
867. Literally: the completion of these things.
868. Your Highness.
869. Alternate translation: deceived. The Latin version reads: *ne quis decipiatur in his deceptiombus.*
870. Literally: people of reflection and wisdom.
871. Literally: according to what he sees.
872. Literally: syllogism or analogy, i.e., science.
873. Literally: who does not know to ascend the path.
874. Literally: sin.
875. Literally: youngsters who paint, i.e., young inexperienced or nonknowledgeable physicians.
876. Literally: occurrences are found.
877. I.e., plethora.
878. Literally: remaining.
879. I.e., to take a mild laxative.
880. Literally: much.
881. Literally: behold.
882. Literally: follow.

883. Morocco or Maghrib.

884. Literally: with full power.

885. The patient fainted.

886. Literally: stand.

887. Literally: grumbling, complaint.

888. Literally: elders of this art. Muntner states that Maimonides is here referring to Abu Youssef Ibn Ayub mentioned by name later in this chapter.

889. Literally: path.

890. Pylorus.

891. According to Muntner, the next several phrases are lacking in the Hebrew version but are found in the Arabic and/or Latin manuscripts.

892. The physician.

893. Literally: sorrow, grief.

894. See note 888 above.

895. Difficulties.

896. Nausea, heartburn, aerophagia?

897. Literally: years.

898. Literally: bitterness.

899. Literally: empty.

900. Literally: hindrance or prevention. This phrase in Hebrew and Arabic is unclear. The Latin version has: *ut extingatur per hoc caliditas febris continue et eius inflammatio sedetur et fervor.*

901. The two patients.

902. Literally: they did not live and did not rise (from their sickbeds).

903. Literally: emptied.

904. Literally: device, stratagem, trick, ruse, artifice.

905. Literally: excessive emptying.

906. Hebrew: *istenis;* sensitiveness, fastidiousness.

907. Your Highness.

908. Literally: rely on.

909. Such as purgation, emesis, diuresis, etc.

910. The great theriac.

911. The theriac of Mithridates.

912. The theriac of Theodorites. Its ingredients are described in the Canon 5: 2:7-11 as follows: aloe, agaric, crocus sativus, acorum pistacia lentis, balsam, euphorbium, long pepper, white pepper, black pepper, gentian, juncus odoratus, costus, teucrium lucidum, epithyme, cassia, scammony, spikenard.

913. Literally: their manner is to effect a powerful therapy.

914. At the right time and in the right dose.

915. Literally: analogy and logic.

916. Morocco.

917. Steinschneider (*Virchow's Archiv f. Patholog. Anat.* Vol. 57, p. 113) states that the Sultan here referred to is Ali ben Yosef ben Mashfim. The Latin manuscript has: *Hachin, Dominus Saracenorum.*

918. Alternate translation: he was ill for sometime.

919. Hebrew: *medina*, literally: land; in Arabic *medina* refers to a city or district rather than a land.

920. Four of his physicians were renowned medical professors.

921. Avenzoar's father who died in 1131.

922. See Steinschneider in *Virchow's Archiv.* Vol. 42 p. 110.

923. Steinschneider adds a fifth famous physician to this list of four: Joseph Ibn Nachmias, also a Jew.

924. He was a Moslem to whom wine is forbidden.

925. Improve the blood circulation.

926. During the night the stomach is empty. The great theriac should only be administered on an empty stomach. Muntner points out that the Arabic version differs somewhat as follows: at the third hour of the day when he took his meal and the theriac had already left his stomach, having been assimilated.

927. Literally: house.

928. Muntner states that Abu Youssef was one of the medical teachers of Maimonides.

929. Should be grandfather.

930. One *zuz*.

931. Here we see Maimonides searching for the truth.

932. Muntner cites the Arabic version: intending to be of use (to mankind) and futher my own knowledge. But they kept silent and that was that.

933. Literally: the opposite of.

934. Literally: increase.

935. Alternate translation: a little less than the (maximum) prescribed amount.

936. The Arabic and Latin versions add: but the dose should not be too small to remove dangerous situations.

937. Maimonides.

938. The death of the Sultan.

939. Literally: intended in the matter.

940. Literally: to jump.

941. Literally: the known manner of medicines.

942. Maimonides is describing the Egyptian approach of avoiding strong medications by using general measures to strengthen the body such as clean air, good food, rest, a comfortable bed and psychological support of the patient by reading or singing or playing music or conversing with him. Maimonides praises this approach for the four reasons he gives below.

943. Literally: I praise.

944. Egyptian physicians.
945. Literally: lost.
946. Compounded laxative medication.
947. Syrup.
948. Convolvulus turpethum.
949. Literally: in these chapters.
950. Galen and Hippocrates lived in cooler climates and therefore appropriately recommended strong measures which are inappropriate and poorly tolerated in hot tropical or subtropical climates.
951. The Sultan Amrael Muselmin.
952. Egyptians.
953. Acute or febrile illnesses?
954. Literally: and their flesh is not thick.
955. Literally: if that is impossible.
956. Literally: produces peace more often than ruin.
957. A mild theriac composed of only four ingredients.
958. Ciminum. Arabic: *kamun*, cumin or caraway.
959. Mentastrum. Arabic: *fudanaj,* mentha.
960. As a method of regular hygiene.
961. Literally: a known error.
962. Literally: harm of the physicians little by little.
963. Alternate translations: indifference, negligence.
964. Since he knows other physicians are also being consulted, he will not give his full effort toward the care of the patient.
965. Literally: there is doubt.
966. Literally: chosen.
967. Literally: man.
968. For many scholars medicine is difficult because of the enormous amount of information to be learned and remembered.
969. Literally: conquer, vanquish, overcome.
970. If physicians wrongly criticize each other before the patient because of professional rivalry.
971. Hebrew: *chazal.* The Arabic version has *chozim* meaning astrologers. Muntner considers this to be a copyist's error.
972. Muntner states that Maimonides does not here refer to Proverbs 10:12 which states *hatred stirs up strife but love covers all transgressions*; rather he refers to the talmudic discussion in tractate *Sanhedrin* folio 105b where it states: love disregards the rule of dignified conduct. This is deduced from Abraham for it is written *And Abraham rose up early in the morning and saddled his ass* (Genesis 22:3). Hate likewise disregards the rule of dignified conduct. This is deduced from Balaam for it is written *And Balaam rose up in the morning and saddled his ass* (Numbers 22:21).
973. Maimonides.
974. Literally: appropriate.
975. Literally: leans by nature to his habits.
976. Literally: leans towards.
977. Literally: be saved from.

978. See *Maimonides' Treatise on Resurrection* (Rosner, translator and editor. New York, Ktav, 1982) for his opinion on the world to come, the Messiah and resurrection.
979. The Arabic manuscript concludes as follows: copy by the son of excellent ability Abu Imram Musa ben Ubaidallah (i.e., Maimonides).

TREATISE ON ASTHMA

BIBLIOGRAPHY

by

JACOB I. DIENSTAG*

I. EDITIONS AND TRANSLATIONS

1931

1. * Altherthum, Hans

    Die Schrift über des Musa ibn Maimun Moses Maimonides nach der lateinischen Übersetzung einer Munchener Handschrift zum l. Male hrsg. 105 s. [MS]. Berlin, Med. Diss. 1927 [1931].

    Listed in G. Kish and K. Roepke, *Schriften zur Geschichte der Juden*. Tübingen: J.C.B. Mohr, 1959, p. 38, no. 315.

1938

2. ספר הקצרת ("ספר המסעדים") מקלה [י'] פי אלרבו מאת... . משה בן מיימון , בתרגומו של הרופא שמואל בנבנשתי איש סרגוסטה. מפורש ומבואר ע״י זיסמן מונטנר. י״ל ע״פ כ״י עברי פריס מ' 1173. ירושלים (חסר שם מדפיס) תרצ״ח. [1] דף; 46 עמ'.

    במהדורה זו אין פרוש ובאור. מהדורה עם פרוש להלן.

1940

3. רבינו משה בן מיימון כתבים רפואיים ערוכים ומסדרים עפ״י כתבי יד עברים ולועזים בצרוף מבואות, פירושים, מפתחות וביבליאוגרפיה לכל ספר וספר על ידי ד״ר זיסמן מונטנר, כרך א: ספר הקצרת או "ספר המסעדים" مقالة في الربو (מקאלה פי אלרבו), בתרגומו

---

*   I wish to thank the Memorial Foundation for Jewish Culture which provided financial support for the preparation of this bibliography.

העברי של הרופא שמואל בנבנשתי איש סרגוסטה עפ"י כ"י פריס מ'
1173, י"ל בפעם הראשונה בצרוף מבוא וביאורים...). ירושלים, ר. מס'
(דפוס המערב), (ת"ש). 167, [1], XV ע', פקסימילים. °8.

עמ' ט-סה: מבוא. — התוכן: ביבליוגרפיה (ט-יא), — פרטים על
ר' שמואל בנבנשתי (יא-יב), — הערכה (יב-יד), — הרופא רבינו
משה בן מימון ומלאכת הרפואה שלו (טו-סה), תמצית התוכן
ותרגום ההקדמה באנגלית.

Added title page: Moshe Ben Maimon (Maimonides). *The Book
on Asthma.* Hebrew translation by the physician Rabbi Shemuel
Benvenishti, the Saragossan (about 1300). Published for the first
time with commentary and explanatory notes by Suessman
Muntner. Jerusalem: Rubin Mass, 1940.

Reviews, appraisals, and comments: S. Kagan, *Bitzaron*, 3 (1941): 453-54
(Hebrew); P. Lachovor, *Kneseth Lezekher Bialick*, 6 (1941): 498-99
(Hebrew); L. Nemoy, *Harofé Haivri; Hebrew Medical Journal*, 13, part 2
(1940): 133-34; Levy, ibid. p. 129-32 (both in Hebrew); A. Levinson,
Medical Leaves, 4 (1942): 219-20; D. Friedman, *Harefuah*, 19, no. 1-2
(July-Aug. 1940): 4-5; J. Unna, *Ha-Zofeh*, August 2, 1940; reprinted in his
Zikhron Yosef (Tel-Aviv, 1983): 243-44.

1953

4.   Tratedo del Asma. In: Cantera Burgos and F. Perez Castro, eds.,
     Antologia Hebraica Postbiblica. Madrid: Facultad de Filosofia y
     Letras Instituto Arias Montano (C.S.I.C.), 1953, 77-79.

Fragment of Hebrew translation, most likely from the Muntner edition.

1960

5.   Una Obra Sobre el Asma en el Siglo XII. *Revista Argentina de
     Alergie*, 7 (1960): 119-126.

Selections in Spanish translation.

1963—1965

6.   רבינו משה בן מיימון, ספר הקצרת או "ספר המסעדים" (מקאלה פי
     אלרבו) בתרגומו העברי של הרופא ר' שמואל בנבנשתי איש סרגוסטה,
     עפ"י כ"י פריס מ' 1173, מהדורה שנייה [צ"ל: שלישית] הוצאה לאור
     ע"י זיסמן מונטנר. ירושלים: הוצאת גניזה, תשכ"ג/1963, 56 עמ'.

     מהדורה מתוקנת בהשמטת הפירוש, הקדמות ומפתחות שבהוצאת ת"ש/1940.

7. *Treatise on Asthma*. Edited by Suessman Muntner. Philadelphia: J.B. Lippincott Co., 1963, XXIV, 115 p., port facsims.

   Preface by Béla Schick; introduction by M. Murray Peshkin.

   Reviews: J.B. Sarner, *J.Q.R.*, n.s., 55 (1965): 90-91; A.S. MacNalty, *British Medical J.* (Feb. 1, 1964): 295; M.B. Etziony, *J. of the History of Medicine*, 19 (1965): 313-14; Francisco Cantera, *Sefarad*, 24, no. 2 (1964): 370-72; Jacob I. Dienstag, *Jewish Social Studies*, 28 (1966): 38-39.

8. Le Traité de l'Asthme de Maïmonide (1135-1204). Traduit pour la première fois em français d'après le texte hébreu par le Prof. Suessman Muntner et le Dr. Isidore Simon. *Rev. d'Histoire de la Médecine Hébraïque,* no. 62 (Dec. 1963): 171-186; nos. 63-66 (1964): 5-13, 83-97, 127-139, 187-196; no. 67 (Mar. 1965): 5-15.

9. ספר הקצרת או "ספר המסעדים" בתרגומו של הרופא ר' שמואל בנבנשתי איש סרגוסטה. יוצא לאור על-פי כתבי-יד ע"י זיסמן מונטנר. ברבינו משה בן מיימון: כתבים רפואיים ערוכים ומסדרים על-פי כתבי-יד... בידי זיסמן מונטנר. כרך רביעי, ירושלים: מוסד הרב קוק, תשכ"ה/1965, עמ' [67]-119.

   זהה עם מהדורת תשכ"ג.

1987

10. ספר הקצרת או "ספר המסעדים" בתרגומו של הרופא ר' שמואל בנבנשתי איש סרגוסטה. יוצא לאור על-פי כתבי-יד ע"י זיסמן מונטנר. ברבינו משה בן מיימון: כתבים רפואיים ערוכים ומסדרים על-פי כתבי-יד... בידי זיסמן מונטנר. כרך רביעי, ירושלים: מוסד הרב קוק, תשמ"ז/1987, עמ' 67-199.

   "הדפסה שנייה...". זהה עם מהדורת תשכ"ה.

1994

11. Moses Maimonides' Treatise on Asthma. Translated into English from Suessman Muntner's Hebrew edition and edited by Fred Rosner. With bibliography by Jacob I. Dienstag. Haifa: Maimonides Research Institute, 1994, 176 p.

II. ESSAYS AND STUDIES

12. Steinschneider, Moritz, 1816-1907

Samuel Benveniste und Maimonides über Asthma, *Hebraeische Bibliographie*, 8 (1865): 85-89.

On Benveniste the translator of the *Treatise on Asthma* into Hebrew.

13. Steinschneider, Moritz, 1816-1907

Die hebräischen Uebersetzungen. Berlin: Kommissionsverlag des Bibliographischen Bureaus, 1893, p. 767-769; reprinted in Graz: Akademische Druck, 1956.

14. Steinschneider, Moritz, 1816-1907

Die arabische Literatur der Juden. Frankfurt a.M.: J. Kauffmann, 1902, p. 215; reprint, Hildesheim: Georg Olms, 1964.

15. Sobernheim, M.

Protokol. *Monatsschrift für Geschichte und Wissenschaft des Judenthums*, 67 (1923): 80.

Concerning a doctoral dissertation on the Latin translation of *the Treatise on Asthma* by Sudhoff.

16. Encyclopaedia Judaica, vol. 4 (Berlin: Eshkol, 1929): 156. Samuel Benveniste.

As translator of the Treatise on Asthma.

17. Weiszberg, Louis, 1912-

Traité de l'Asthma. In his *Esquisse de l'oeuvre, Médicale Maïmonide*. Paris: L. Rodstein, 1939, p. 15-16.

18.   לוי, אברהם יהודה, 1896-1949

הערות לספר הקצרת להרמב״ם. **הרופא העברי**, 13, חוברת ב׳ (1940):
129-132.

הערות על מהדורת מונטנר משנת ת״ש/1940

19.   מונטנר, זיסמן, 1897-1973
לקורות השפה העברית כשפת הלימוד בחכמת הרפואה. ירושלים:
גניזה, ת"ש 1940, עמ' 83-85..

20.   Meyerhof, Max, 1874-1945
The Medical Work of Maimonides. In Salo W. Baron, ed. *Essays on Maimonides*. New York: Columbia University Press, 1941, p. 278-79

21.   אבנרי, צבי
שמואל בנבנשתי. **האנציקלופדיה העברית**, ט, ירושלים (תש"ך/1960):
48.
על מתרגם **ספר הקצרת**.

22.   Bar-Sela, Ariel, 1930-1990;
Hebbel E. Hoff and Elias Faris, died 1960
introduction to *Moses Maimonides' Two Treatises on the Regimen of Health. Transactions of the American Philosophical Society*, 54, part 4 (July, 1964): 8.

23.   Olbert, Th.
Das Asthma Bronchiale im werke des Maimonides. *Medizinische Welt*, 1965: 2714-2716.

24.   Rosner, Fred, 1935-
Moses Maimonides' Treatise on Asthma. *Medical Times*, 94 (1966): 1227-1230.

25.   Muntner, Suessmann, 1897-1973
Maimonides' Treatise on Asthma. *Diseases of the Chest*, 54 (August 1968): 128-132.

26.   Rosner, Fred, 1935-
Moses Maimonides' *Treatise on Asthma. Thorax*, 36, no. 4, (April 1981): 245-251.

27. Sakula, A.

Moses Maimonides' Treatise on Asthma [letter]. *Thorax*, 36, no. 7 (July 1981): 560.

28. Ackermann, Hermann, 1954-

Die Gesundheitslehre des Maimonides: medizinische, ethische umd religionsphilosophische Aspekte. Diss. Ruprrcht-Karls-Universität zu Heidelberg, 1982, p. 43-45.

29. Rosner, Fred, 1935-

Moses Maimonides' *Treatise on Asthma. Journal of Asthma*, 21, no. 2 (April 1984): 119-129.

"Espanded and modified with permission from paper originally published in *Thorax* , 36: 245-251."

30. Rosner, Fred, 1935-

Moses Maimonides' Treatise on Asthma. In: Tillem, ed., *The 1986 Jewish Directory and Almanac*. New York: Pacific Press, 1985, p. 295-301.

31. Dienstag, Jaob I.

Bibliography of Maimonides' *Treatise on Asthma*. In: *Moses Maimonides' Treatise on Asthma*. Translated into English from Susseman Muntner's Hebrew edition and edited by Fred Rosner. Haifa: Maimonides Research Institute, 1994, p. 161-170.

32. Rosner, Fred, 1935-

Summary and appreciation of Maimonides' *Treatise on Asthma*. In: *Moses Maimonides' Treatise on Asthma*. Translated into English from Susseman Muntner's Hebrew edition and edited by Fred Rosner. Haifa: Maimonides Research Institute, 1994, p. 29-40.

III. BIBLIOGRAPHICAL REFERENCES
TO MANUSCRIPTS

33. Rossi, Giovanni Bernardo de, 1742-1831
    Mss. Codices Hebraici Biblioth. I. B. de-Rossi... Accedit
    appendix qua continentur mss. condices reliqui al. linguarum.
    Parmae, 1803, cod, 1280.
    "Collection passed into possession of R. Biblioteca Palatina, Parma." (S.
    Shunami, Bibl. of Jew. Bibliographies, 1965, no. 3078).

34. Krafft, Albrecht & Deutsch, Simon, 1822-1877
    Die handschriftlichen hebräischen Werke der k.k. Hofbiblio-
    thek zu Wien. Wien, 1847, no. CLI.

35. Goldenthal, Jacob, 1815-1868
    Die neuerworbenen handschriftlichen hebräischen Werke der
    k.k. Hofbibliothek zu Wien, beschrieben semmt Ergänzungen
    zum Krafft'schen Catalog. Wien, 1851, p. 88-89.

36. Steinschneider, Moritz, 1816-1907
    Catalogus Librorum hebraeorum in Bibliotheca Bodleiana.
    Berolini, 1852-60, col. 1919; reprints, Berlin, 1931; Hildesheim:
    Georg Olms, 1964.

37. Steinschneider, Moritz, 1816-1907
    [Note]. *Hebräische Bibliographie*, 4 (1861): 141, note.

38. Zotenberg, Hirsch
    *Catalogues des Manuscrits Hébreux et Samaritains de la
    Bibliothèque Impériale.* Paris, 1866, no. 1173 (2); 1175 (1); 1176
    (2); 1211.

39. Steinschneider, Moritz, 1816-1907
    *Die hebräischen Handschriften der k. Hof- und Staatsbibliothek in
    München.* München, 1875, nos. 43 (4); 280 (1); zweite grossenteils
    umgearbeitete und erweiterte Auflage. München, 1895.

40. Steinschneider, Moritz, 1816-1907
Verzeichnis der hebräischen Handschriften der (Abt. [1]-2).
Berlin: A. Ascher, 1878-1897, nos. 232 (3).
(Die Handschriften-Verzeichnisse der Königlichen Bibliothek
zu Berlin. Band 2.).

41. Modona, Leonnello, 1841-1902
Catalogo dei Codici Ebraici della Biblioteca della R. Università
di Bologna. Firenze, 1889, no. 20 (5).

42. Steinschneider, Moritz, 1816-1907
Die arabische Literatur dee Juden. Frankfurt a.M.: J.
Kauffmann, 1902, p. 215; reprint, Hildesheim: Georg Olms,
1964.

43. Marx, Alexander, 1878-1953
Review of M.R. James, *Descriptive Catalogue of the Manuscripts
in the Library of St. John's College.* Cambridge University Press,
1913. *Jewish Quarterly Review*, n s, 9 (1919): 255.

44. Thorndike, Lynn, 1882-1965
A History of Magic and Experimental Science, vol. 2. New York:
Columbia University Press, 1923, p. 205, note 2.

45.   מונטנר, זיסמן, 1897-1973
ביבליוגרפיה. ב״מבוא״ **לספר הקצרת** לרבינו משה בן מיימון, ירושלים:
ראובן מס, ת״ש עמ׳ ט-יא.

46.   בית־אריה, מ., 1937-
תרגומים בלתי־ידועים של ספרי רפואה לרמב״ם. **קרית ספר**, 38
(3691/ג) תשכ״ג: 567.

כתב־יד הספרים האוניברסיטאי 3941 °Heb. 8 המכיל בחלקו המכריע ארבעה
מכתביו הרפואיים של הרמב״ם בתרגומים עבריים בלתי־ידועים; נספחים: השוואות
התרגומים בכתב־יד לתרגומים האחרים, עמ׳ 573.

47. Freimann, Aaron, 1871-1948

Union Catalogue of Hebrew Manuscripts and their Location, vol. 2. New York: American Academy for Jewish Research, 1964, nos. 4532; 4810/1; 5670; 9566; 9762; 9797.

48. Loewe, Raphael, 1919-

Hebrew Books and "Judaica" in Mediaeval Oxford and Cambridge. *Remember the Days... essays presented to Cecil Roth*. London: Jewish Historical Society of England [1966], p. 48.

49. Schwartz, Arthur Zacharias, 1880-1939 and
Löwinger, David Samuel, 1904-

Die hebräischen Handschriften in Osterreich. (Ausserhalb der Nationalbibliothek in Wien). New York: American Academy for Jewish Research, 1973, no. 296 (1).

50. Beit-Arié, M., 1937-

A Palaeographic Description of the Jerusalem Hebrew Manuscript. In: J. O. Leibowitz and S. Marcus, eds. *Moses Maimonides on the Causes of Symptoms*. Berkeley: University of California Press, 1974, p. 35 (top).

Manuscript heb. 8° 3941 of the Jewish National and University Library in Jerusalem (Fol. 20 r-78 v) which consists of a translation of the *Treatise* which "differs from both the popular translation of Samuel Benvenisti (edited by Muntner, 1940) and the lesser known translation of Joshua Shatibi (Steinschneider [*Die hebräischen Handschriften...* München], 1875, no. 280)".

★★★

For additional references, see the introductions to the *Treatise* and the studies in section II.

VI. INDEX TO AUTHORS, EDITORS
AND TRANSLATORS

INDEX